History of the
American Academy
of Optometry

History
of the
American Academy
of Optometry

1922–1986

BY JAMES R. GREGG, O.D.

1987
American Academy of Optometry

DEDICATION

As institutions go, the American Academy of Optometry is a youngster. Barely a third the age of the Republic itself, the Academy is still new enough that many of its members are older than it is, and little that is recorded in this history is without a living witness.

In its sixty-six years the Academy has grown from a small nucleus of idealists with a vision of what optometry could become, to a vital organization with a worldwide membership. Nevertheless, its mission remains essentially what the founders set forth: to foster research, education, and clinical excellence. Adherence to these goals has shaped the Academy's history and made the Academy an exemplar for the profession.

Many individuals have played a part in the progress of the Academy as an organization. But it is the thousands of practitioner, researcher, and educator members who have kept its spirit and its purpose alive. They are the ones who have shared their insights and discoveries, knowing that the free and open exchange of ideas is the lifeblood of a profession.

To them, with appreciation and with admiration, this history is respectfully dedicated.

Preface

This book represents my interpretation of the first sixty-five years of the American Academy of Optometry. I have written it in a way I felt would make it good reading, if indeed history can be "good" reading. At the same time, I have attempted to produce an accurate and documented record of the birth and growth of the Academy that will prove useful for reference. Hopefully I have come close to a reasonable balance between a popular and scholarly version.

Though I have been a member of the Academy for nearly two-thirds of its life, I have not relied on my memory to write this book. Fortunately there exists much information in printed form. The very early days are recorded in materials published by the Academy itself. For forty years or so, many other optometric publications published considerable news about the Academy. Though actual minutes and original documents were scarce until about the 1960s, from then on the Academy files contain an increasing volume of official material describing the Academy's activities. Thus as news about the Academy began to appear less frequently in the press, the official record began to provide increasing information.

A mountain of material was available for reference in writing this history. A complete set of the journals published by the Academy is in the Library of the Southern California College of Optometry (SCCO) as are the thirteen volumes of the *Transactions of the American Academy of Optometry*. The International Library and Archives of Optometry (ILAMO) in St. Louis, besides having its own collection of journals and historical documents, became the depository for archival materials for the Academy, including a series of "living history"videotapes. The Academy office in Washington also houses many records, particularly those concerning the past decade or so.

Many individuals, including a number of past presidents, supplied copies of correspondence, articles, and personal recollections about the Academy and its activities. Besides that, correspondence and personal discussions with dozens of Academy members provided interesting insights. The manuscript was reviewed by members of the AAO History Committee and parts were read by several other individuals. Thus the base of information was broad and varied. The problem was trying to put the story together in one volume of realistic size.

A vast amount of material had to be condensed. The squeezing process eliminated many noteworthy events and no doubt the contributions of some individuals to the history of the Academy. It is obvious that not everything could be included, and many people and activities could only be briefly mentioned. This is unfortunate, since it may seem to minimize the importance of some events, as well as the names and accomplishments of some individuals in the opinion of certain readers. I share their concern. Often I wanted to write more but there was simply not room. The decision as to what to put in or leave out was totally mine.

The purpose of this book is to tell the story of the Academy's origin and development, not to serve as a vehicle to pay tribute to individuals. However, that cannot and should not be avoided entirely. Some individuals stand out because of the length of their service or the nature of their accomplishments. Some deserve more credit than others. But deciding which event or person to highlight and which to minimize, or even ignore, was gnashingly difficult. Hopefully I have been reasonably objective and have not made too many bad choices.

Though the background material was voluminous, in some instances it was incomplete and occasionally inconsistent. There are likely some errors in dates, names, and facts reported here. Certainly whatever oversights, misinterpretations, or unfairness may seem to appear, none is intentional. I take full responsibility for what is written. It has not been "approved" by anyone and certainly is not an official statement of the Academy.

But I did not produce this book alone. The toughest part about naming individuals is to avoid leaving out any who truly deserve credit. Unfortunately that is probably not possible. The whole process began with the interest, and then action, of James Leeds in getting the writing of a history started. President Melvin Wolfberg, along with his Executive Council, supported the idea and the plan of the project was approved. Henry Knoll, Ralph Wick, and Harold Simmerman, members of the AAO History Committee, provided suggestions and assistance.

Big accolades must go to Maria Dablemont, Librarian at ILAMO, and her staff, who put up with weeks of on-site research and general disruption of their routine. But their enthusiasm and assistance made the task much easier. The same is true of Patricia Carlson, Librarian at SCCO, and her staff, who always met requests for hard-to-find materials with a smile.

Then there were many individuals who provided special help — Morris Kirschen, Henry Peters, Frank Brazelton, Robert Baxter, Meredith Morgan, Dan Hummel, Walter Chase, and David Lewis to name a few. My thanks to all of them.

But there is one person who richly deserves lavish praise. That is Bernice Gregg. She spent countless hours doing research in Southern California and St. Louis, checking details, chasing down small facts and correct spelling of names, putting the manuscript on computer, and typing in all of the changes. There was some worry at times about when it would get done and how it would all turn out. But thanks especially to Bernice, the project was completed on time and hopefully is a success as well.

The many dedicated members of the American Academy of Optometry, particularly those in leadership roles, deserve great credit for creating an academy that has played a very significant role in the field of vision care. They are truly the heroes of this story.

JAMES R. GREGG

June 1987
Anaheim, California

Table of Contents

History
of the
American Academy
of Optometry

CHAPTER 1

The Beginnings of
Optometric Academies

I n a sense, the American Academy of Optometry (AAO) actually had its beginnings in 1898. That was when the American Association of Opticians was formed, the organization that became the present-day American Optometric Association (AOA).[1]

The formation of a national organization brought together members of the profession specifically to plan for improvement in optometry. There were many issues to be faced — political, legislative, ethical, public education about vision care, practice development, and much more. Raising educational and scientific standards was high on the priority list. In fact, only a few years after its birth, the infant AOA* began to address the matter of some sort of "academy" or "college" designed to provide high-level postgraduate education and certification of the qualifications of its members.

But optometric education was by no means standardized or organized in the early 1900s. There were no laws regulating optometry until 1901. There were about sixty schools teaching optometry, with some courses lasting only two weeks. No optometrist had to prove ability to practice. There were very few opportunities for additional education. Public understanding of vision care and certainly the stature of optometry were pitifully low.

Still, many optometrists were conscientious and competent, at least in terms of the education and the tools available at the time. Unfortunately others were "spec peddlers." There were some in both groups, professionals and commercialists, who objected to meeting rigorous

---

* The American Optometric Association is designated by the acronym AOA, and the American Academy of Optometry by AAO throughout this book. Actually the American Optometric Association was called the American Association of Opticians (AAO) from 1898 to 1910, when it was changed to the American Optical Association (AOA), then to the American Optometric Association in 1919.

standards. That is no different than the situation in the development of other health-care professions. Even in the mid-1980s, certification of clinical competency in optometry is a hotly debated issue.

Consider the factors that the young profession had to evaluate in deciding where to direct its energies in the early 1900s:

1. Legislation to regulate practice was of critical importance. Even by 1920, four states and the District of Columbia had no optometry laws.

2. The new organization of optometrists itself had to gain experience and develop leadership. For nearly the first two decades, all of the work was done by volunteers with little or no staff support.

3. The number of optometrists in the AOA was small. Building membership and developing the organization required considerable time and attention before another entity, such as an academy, could be adequately supported.

4. As a scientific discipline, optometry was ill-defined. There was no organization of optometric educational institutions until the early 1920s. Optometric educators had very little involvement in the AOA until about that same time. Indeed, the concern and interest in setting up an "academy" came primarily from practitioners.

These factors, and others, explain why attempts to establish an educational and scientific body were relatively unsuccessful in the early years. The need for it was recognized by many of optometry's leaders, and the struggle to form an academy continued with ups and down from the very beginning.

In 1901 at the AOA Congress in Chicago, President A.J. Cross proposed the establishment of the American Optical College.[2] The issue was debated for several hours, and finally the discussion was terminated by the appointment of a committee of five to study the idea and make recommendations. The proposal was to set up a "college" that would give examinations in various subjects. The college was to provide a form of certification so that passing its examinations would be an indication of proficiency. The plan resembled certification of specialties that was still being considered by the AOA nearly eighty-five years later.

The committee report on the "paper college," as it came to be called, stated that the idea seemed to be a good one but the details should be worked out by a board of regents. In the year that followed, the optometric press was full of pro and con opinions about the college. However the "paper college" proposed by Cross never materialized. The

Board of Regents, after studying the proposal, actually recommended against the AOA sponsoring a college (or academy), stating that the Association was in no position nor had any right to do so. The regents had made a sincere effort to carry out the mandate given them, but in spite of this, felt they must recommend against it. Instead, they submitted another idea:[3]

> Resolved, that an organization entitled "The Physiological Branch of the A.O.A." be formed of such refractionists as have already shown their interest in this branch of the work by having submitted a thesis as prescribed by the board of regents, and such others who desire to become members, who shall conform to the requirements for membership in said physiologic branch as may be determined upon. The object of this branch shall be to stimulate the desire for the more technical and scientific equipment in the field of physiologic optometry, and to recognize high attainment in this branch by the conferring of some suitable honor upon those being found worthy of this distinction, similar to that awarded by the various scientific academies.

Thus was born the Physiological Branch which was to make up the educational program of the Association for nearly two decades.* This turned out to be one of the most significant steps taken by the fledgling association.

The Physiological Branch set up its own constitution and bylaws and elected officers. It was in this Physiological Branch that the AOA library got its start. But the Branch was somewhat of a disappointment. Membership was small and by 1904 had accomplished very little.

On November 15, 1905, E. LeRoy Ryer, president of the Optical Society of the City of New York, addressed a meeting of the group, and proposed the establishment of an "American Academy of Optometry."[4] The fundamental idea was certification. The Academy would give examinations and issue certificates of membership. Each member also was "once each year to do some original work and make a report of the results." Ryer asked if there existed any organization that "does justice to the superior class of intelligence, have we any that offers sufficient reward to warrant men striving to attain membership, have we any that

---

* From 1902 to 1904 the term Physiological Branch was used. In 1904 the name was changed to Physiological Section; then in 1908 it became the Scientific Section.

draws a real distinction between the well and poorly educated?"
Ryer's proposal included some of the points involved:[5]

Membership in this is not to interfere in any sense with
membership in any or all other societies.

Entrance examination to be of so high a standard that
passing it will be sufficient evidence that applicant is fully
qualified to practice optometry.

The reward offered in the way of credentials to be of sufficient value to repay the recipient for the study required to gain
entrance.

Provision to be made to stimulate original research and
foster carefully organized thought upon optometrical subjects.

Aim to bring into closer union the best minds engaged in the
calling throughout the United States, making possible thereby
an interchange of ideas that will broaden views and eliminate
narrow, bigoted notions.

Make it imperative that each member once each year do
some original work and make a report of the results.

At each meeting a vote be taken as to what is the most vital
optometrical question confronting the profession at that time.
This agreed upon, let each member work upon it and contribute all that is possible at the next meeting, the reports to be
discussed and condensed and the total results widely and unre-
strictedly published for the benefit of the profession at large.
Thus the knowledge of the best men in the country can be
concentrated and employed to the very greatest advantage.
This organization throughout is bound to surpass any individual efforts, and will prove our strongest argument in favor of
legislation.

Though phrased differently than the purposes of the American
Academy of Optometry were when it was founded, Ryer's proposal in
essence contained the same general concept that describes the Academy today. There was no mention of ethics or standards of practice
included in 1905; however, these elements became significant in the
Academy's goals from its very beginning.

Optometric groups around the nation were busy with arguments for
and against the academy idea in the months that followed. Cross
claimed that it was strangely reminiscent of his "paper college" that
went nowhere in 1901.[6] Certainly again there was growing awareness in
the profession that something must be done about determining quali-

fications to practice. The real problems were related to making a distinction established by an academy and meaningful to the public, so consumers of vision could distinguish good from bad optometrists. There were those who felt that the most effective method would be to put the energies of the profession into legislation and thus physically prevent practice by the unqualified.

John C. Eberhardt, an AOA past president, in an article entitled "The American Academy of Optometry" in 1906, urged that an academy be supported and that it would be very desirable for the profession, stating "An organization making a standard of capacity prerequisite to membership, and devoted to the cause of using its influence toward the elevation and advancement of the science of optometry, can be productive of good, and all should pledge their best efforts to the proposed movement."[7]

In that same year, John Ellis, president of the AOA, addressed the Indiana Optometric Association, also strongly favoring formation of the Academy.[8] A.J. Stoessel, president of the Wisconsin Association of Optometrists, opposed the idea and he put his thoughts very plainly:[9]

> To the Editor: — Pursuant to your request, I shall give you a few of the many reasons why I do not consider an organization like the proposed American Academy of Optometry advisable. In doing so, I know that an awful fate awaits me, since Mr. LeRoy Ryer, with most magnificent audacity, disposes of any intended criticism of his pet scheme beforehand by classing his critics as "shallow minds, afraid to be separated from the really deep minds." Now, is it not fact that men who mistake "their superficial knowledge for real knowledge" are just the ones that are forever striving to band themselves in *select* societies and have that "holier than thou" feeling that the possession of a membership certificate gives them? Men really capable of original research on scientific lines need no society stimulus. Such men have at all times been the most retiring, and have labored quietly and then given the results of their investigations to the world without flaring of trumpets and beating of drums. Real merit is its own reward and can take care of itself without "academy" label.

W. T. Eisensmith, who only two years later became chancellor of the AOA's Scientific Section, also opposed the academy, but for different reasons.[10]

It has long been my desire to see an exclusive scientific association of optometrists in this country, one establishing a national standard of competency, and I have expected that the Physiological or Optometrical Section, as it is now called, of the American Association of Opticians would have filled this long-felt want, and I believe that plans are in consideration by the Board of Regents which will have a tendency to place this Optometrical Section of the American Association on a much higher scientific basis, and if possible to supply this long-felt want in the near future. I do not believe it would be wise to organize another association under the name of the American Optometrical Academy as we have too many associations now, and would have a more or less demoralizing effect upon those in existence, but, as stated above, the Optometrical Section of the American Association should so formulate plans and by-laws which would establish a national standard of competency whereby its members would feel proud, and many others anxious to be one of them.

So there were strong differences of opinion about academies, proficiency certification, and such matters. There was general agreement about the need for education, raising standards and convincing the public of the qualifications of optometry, but methods to achieve those goals were diverse and divisive. These facts partly account for the time it took for a full-fledged academy to develop, and for its slow, early growth. Even today there is far from universal agreement on how goals of an academy should be achieved.

The idea of an academy however was to continue for some time. In a sense, the Physiological Section might have achieved this purpose; but it had only a few members. At the 1906 AOA Convention Ryer made the same proposal in an address before the Physiological Section. Ryer became active in the Section and was elected its president. Ryer himself would become a prominent figure in the Academy when it was established in the 1920s. Some believed that a separate body was necessary, one not dominated by the AOA. The problem seemed clear, but the solution was more elusive.

The Physiological Section of the AOA continued to struggle for existence. Applicants' theses were being read and approved or disapproved. Eleven new members were certified in 1906. Two big steps were taken at the convention. The Physiological Section was completely overhauled. President Ryer made a long address about the Section and

CAREL C. KOCH

Chairman 1929
Secretary 1922–1925; 1944–1973
Journal Editor 1924–1968

Organizations like the American Academy of Optometry are generally easier to create than they are to sustain. When they do
survive and flourish, it is often due to the dedication, skill and
leadership of one person. For the AAO that individual was Carel
C. Koch. He was present when a permanent organization was
formed and became its first secretary. From that time on, in 1922,
until November 1973, he had some significant role to play in the
affairs of the Academy — thirty-seven years as a member of the
Executive Council (secretary, chairman or council
member) and eighteen as editor of the *Journal*
while not an officer or council member.

its problems. He pointed out that it had only 100 members out of a possible 5000. Some prominent past presidents did not belong to the Section. He believed its founding was premature and that the name "Physiological" was wrong. The result was a change in name in 1908 to the Scientific Section, with a completely new constitution and bylaws. There would be no dues but a thesis was still required for membership. W. T. Eisensmith of Charleston, West Virginia, was elected chancellor of the new Scientific Section. The constitution of the Section briefly described its purpose:[11]

> Art. 1. This body shall be known as the Scientific Section of the American Optical Association.
> Art. 2. The object of this body shall be to stimulate and encourage higher standards of proficiency in the science of Optometry, incite analytical investigation, record results of such research as may prove of value and recognize merit in this field by conferring upon those found worthy the degree of Fellow of Optometrical Science. *
> Art. 3. Any person engaged in the profession of optometry complying with the provision of this section shall be eligible for membership.
> Art. 4. The officers of this section shall be a Chancellor, Vice-Chancellor, registrar, and librarian, who shall be elected by the members of the Scientific Section during the annual meeting of the American Optical Association, to serve for a term of one year.

The 1919 Congress marked the end of the Scientific Section. It had a hard life; but the Section planted the seeds that would develop into entities that would achieve some of its early goals. The Scientific Section was replaced with a Department of Education. The Section's attempt at "certification" by means of a thesis requirement may have been the cause of its failure. The idea was sound but premature.

In spite of the Physiological Section trying to fill a need, it was not doing so — at least in the minds of some. So a National Academy of Optometry was formed in 1912.[12] It is not clear exactly how it started or who its officers were. It apparently was the idea and work of one man, Eugene G. Wiseman. He is shown as president in the published mate-

---

* It is interesting to note that it was proposed to confer a "degree" upon those found "worthy." At no other time did any section of the AOA or any of the various academies propose to award a degree.

ials but no other names are mentioned. Strangely enough this is the same man who 15 years later became the second chairman of the American Academy of Optometry and held the office for five years. Wiseman certainly was one of the most dominant figures — if not *the* most dominant — in its very early success. *

An article March 28, 1912, by Wiseman, described in detail why he felt an academy was needed. Here is an excerpt from the article:[13]

> In organizing and launching the National Academy of Optometry the men most interested are sincere and earnest in their belief that in this organization they have constructed a vehicle which is the *sine qua non* of consistent, efficient and rapid optometric progress and growth. They have carefully reviewed the fundamental principles governing optical organizations of today in this country and have as carefully considered the optical and optometric conditions in their entirety.
>
> The net result has been the reluctant but nevertheless forceful realization that there were many necessary features lacking in our present societies, and that these, by the nature of things, could not be supplied by the organizations in question.
>
> With this realization they have endeavored to construct an organization which will supply these deficiencies and yet in no way be antagonistic to other optical organizations. To successfully accomplish this end, much time and thought have necessarily been devoted to the manifold elements which demand consideration, and no new feature has been embodied in the constitution and bylaws without realizing, first its need in the past, then its effect in the immediate present and finally its possible result in the future.

Wiseman went on to explain the design of the proposed academy and how it would function, pointing out that in no way did he intend it to be antagonistic to the AOA. Dues were to be $3 per year after a $2 initiation fee. Included was a constitution and bylaws which defined its purpose as follows: Its object shall be to advance optometric science and extend optometric knowledge, to elevate the standard of optometric education, to promote optometric legislation favorable to its members and to the public, to promote friendly intercourse among its members, and to found an accredited body of skilled practitioners in the profession of optometry.

* Wiseman was awarded an Honorary Life Fellowship by the Academy in 1962.

A month later plans were announced to make the National Academy of Optometry permanent at the AOA Convention in Chicago in 1912.[14] Examinations for membership were announced to be given in June. A few weeks later an article appeared appealing for members and again explaining the purpose of the Academy:[15]

> But to accomplish these great ends we must have men — 1,000, yes 2,000 of them. And you men who read this are the men we want. Do not think we mean somebody else. You must contribute your share if you want to share in the results.
>
> Be not like one man who wrote, "When I see the Academy is sure of success, I'll join." Translated, his words read, "After you fellows have done all the work, spent all the money and placed the Academy on such footing that I risk nothing but gain all when I come in, I'll join."

Two weeks later the Journal and Review published a letter from Wiseman and a copy of the application blank for membership which included a certificate of moral character.[16] E.G. Wiseman certainly tried as hard as he knew how to start an academy but to no avail. In a typewritten copy of his autobiography, Wiseman mentions several other men who were interested in the academy he attempted to organize but none are listed as officers, nor does he indicate it was ever anything but a personal effort.[17] He attempted to combine his academy of about 100 members with the Scientific Section of the AOA but was flatly rebuffed by A.J. Cross, John Eberhardt and Charles Prentice. The National Academy came to an end with this letter to the members.[18]

> Dear Sir:
>
> Owing to the following acts I have deemed it advisable to discontinue my activities in regard to the National Academy of Optometry:
>
> *First* — While a great many optometrists seemed to favor the proposition, most of whom were members of State Board Examiners in Optometry and officers in State and local societies, relatively few had the courage of their convictions and joined the academy.
>
> *Second* — The great burden of work fell upon my shoulders and too few members of the academy evinced a desire to aid me. I was willing to sacrifice a great deal to make a success of the organization and did actually sacrifice a great deal of time, effort and money, but my

efforts were seemingly so little appreciated that I have decided to abandon the work.

Third — Our activities resulted in effectively waking up the Scientific Section of the AOA with the result that it is now accomplishing much which we set out to do, although there is still much to be desired.

There still remains in the treasury of the society a little less than 20 percent of the gross amount paid in, and I am herewith returning to you your pro rata share. The remainder was spent in circulars, stationery, stamps, etc., and you may regard it as having been spent for a very worthy cause, since our efforts have greatly contributed toward the awakening of optometrists concerning the needs of their organizations.

Thanking you for the aid you have rendered and with best wishes for your continued success, I am

E.G. Wiseman

That was the end of any known attempts to establish a national academy until 1922. However, there were several academies of optometry founded on a local basis and they functioned to some degree prior to that time. Their history is difficult to document and their degree of success and longevity is uncertain, but a few are described here.

The New York Academy of Optometry was organized by R.M. Lockwood, E. LeRoy Ryer, E.E. Hotaling, N.Y. Hull and J.H. Drakeford. A meeting of charter members was held in New York on February 7, 1913.[19] Passage of an examination was required for membership as well as adherence to the Code of Ethics which was spelled out "It shall be the duty of each member to conduct the practice of optometry in a legitimate and professional manner."* Clinical proficiency and ethical behavior were thus requirements for membership much the same as the American Academy would require a decade later.

In 1914 some optometrists organized the Pennsylvania College of Optometrists, although at that time it was not a college in the usual sense, rather "an association of learned men." It functioned as an educational group much like an "academy." Its purpose was also partly political. It was designed to help fight some of the legislative and court battles occurring at that time. This is described in detail in Albert Fitch's *My Fifty Years in Optometry.*[20]

---

* Thus as early as 1913 ethical standards — though very loosely defined— were required for membership in an optometric academy.

The Virginia Academy of Optometry was formed in 1915, though apparently little activity took place until 1919 when papers were presented at its annual meeting. In 1930 an article in the *Optical Journal and Review* reported it held its quarterly meeting in Richmond, stating, "The Academy has steadily pursued educational work during its eleven years of activity. Under its inspiration, members have contributed much of value in furthering helpful study and research."[21]

There were a few more "academies" prior to 1920 but little is known of them. There is brief mention of a meeting of an academy in Southern California in 1911 but no information available as to its organizational nature.[22] A Cleveland Academy of Optometry was formed in 1916, but no more is known about it.[23]

In the 1920s several more academies were organized: the San Francisco Academy in 1922,[24] The North Carolina Academy of Optometry in 1924,[25] and the Oregon Academy of Optometry in 1925.[26] These were not chapters of the American Academy (it did not grant charters to affiliate chapters until 1929), but separate organizations, and there were most likely a few others. *

That brief review of the struggle of the profession to accomplish certain objectives in regard to education and ethical behavior delineates some reasons why the American Academy of Optometry developed as it did. It accounts to some degree for the existence of a separate American Optometric Association and an American Academy of Optometry. It indicates also the factors that accounted for different leadership of the two organizations. The next chapter elaborates further on these same forces at work in the early years of the AAO.

It seems clear that the time was ripe in the early 1920s for the formation of a national academy of optometry that would become successful. In spite of all the lofty things that had been said and written about the need for a learned body to develop the science of optometry and upgrade education, "dissatisfaction with the commercial state of the profession"[27] was a major motivating factor on the part of the men who founded the American Academy of Optometry. Adoption of a code of ethics was an early order of business. But education was a principal goal as well, and the Academy began immediately to develop ways to fill the needs and achieve the goals that had been established during the

---

* Brief notes appear in various optometric magazines about the St. Louis Academy, the Interstate Academy (Northwestern New York and Northeastern Pennsylvania), the Essex County Academy, the Vanderburgh Academy (tri-state area of Indiana, Illinois and Kentucky), and the Philadelphia Academy, but there are so few details it is not possible to determine any significant facts about them.

past quarter of a century by the profession of optometry.

But it would be a long and time-consuming process. Sixty-five years later the Academy would hardly resemble the concept of its founders. It would have achieved many of the goals, but the explosion of knowledge in the field of vision care, the changing character of health care delivery systems, and status of the health care professions in society, would present continuing challenges, and re-evaluation of goals and methods to achieve them. The pages that follow describe how the American Academy of Optometry was born and developed, and how it became a very significant force in the optometric profession.

REFERENCES*

1. Gregg JR. American Optometric Association: A History. St. Louis: Am Optom Assoc, 1972:10.
2. American Association of Opticians meets in Chicago. Opt J, Sept 1901;8:849.
3. Gregg JR. American Optometric Association: A History. St. Louis: Am Optom Assoc, 1972:20-21.
4. Academy of optometry proposed. Jewelers Circular Weekly, Nov 29, 1905;51 (18):101.
5. Ryer EL. The National Academy of Optometry. Opt J, Aug 16, 1906;18(8): 465-467.
6. Gregg JR. American Optometric Association: A History. St. Louis: Am Optom Assoc, 1972:31.
7. Eberhardt JC. The American Academy of Optometry. Opt J, Feb 1, 1906;17(6): 364-365.
8. Annual address of President J.H. Ellis before the Indiana Optical Society, Feb 20, 1906. Opt J, Mar 1, 1906;17(10):527-531.
9. Stoessel SJ. Against the Optometrical Academy. Opt J, Mar 1, 1906;17(10):401.
10. Eisensmith WT. An optometrical academy not needed. Opt J, Mar 1, 1906;17 (10):398.
11. Registrar Arnold invites A.O.A. members to join the Scientific Section. Opt J Rev Optom, Sept 28, 1911;28(13):754.
12. The National Academy of Optometry. Opt J Rev Optom, Apr 25, 1912; 29(18): 1082-1083.
13. Wiseman EG. The National Academy of Optometry. Opt J Rev Optom, Mar 28, 1912; 29(14):838-841.
14. Wiseman explains plans of Academy of Optometry — permanent organization to be effected at Chicago Convention. Opt J Rev Optom, Apr 25, 1912;29(18): 1082-1083.

*Included in the references where appropriate are the months (preceeding the year as is the customary way of recording historical dates) even though they are not necessary in locating an item in pages numbered consecutively throughout an entire volume. The reason for this is that it adds some historical time perspective not easily determined by page numbers alone. Also the issue number is included even though that too is not absolutely necessary. The reason being that it also may improve the time perspective and make it easier to locate a reference in a case where journal issues are not bound into a single volume.

15. National Academy calls for more members. Opt J Rev Optom, May 9, 1912; 29(20):1182-1183.
16. National Academy sends out letters and application blanks. Opt J Rev Optom, May 23, 1912;29(22):1302.
17. Typed autobiography of E.G. Wiseman 1967. Archives of the AAO, ILAMO, St. Louis.
18. Wiseman EG. National Academy of Optometry discontinued. Opt J Rev Optom, June 25, 1914;34(1):58.
19. New York Academy of Optometry organized. Opt J Rev Optom, Feb 13, 1913;31 (8):499.
20. Fitch A. My fifty years in optometry. Philadelphia: Penn. State College Optom, 1955:vol I:30-44.
21. Virginia Academy's annual session. Opt J Rev Optom, Apr 4, 1930;65(4):36.
22. Interesting clinic conducted by Dr. Polasky before Southern California Academy of Optometry. Opt J Rev Optom, Mar 2, 1911;27(10):592.
23. Announcing the Cleveland Academy of Optometry. The Optometrist and the Optician, Jan 1916;16(1):691.
24. San Francisco Academy organized. Opt J Rev Optom, Nov 9, 1922;50(19):44.
25. North Carolina Optometrists form academy. Opt J Rev Optom, Mar 20, 1924;53 (12):55.
26. Oregon Academy of Optometry. Optom Weekly, Aug 27, 1925;16(25):1106.
27. Leeds JP. Review of the transactions of the American Academy of Optometry. Amer J Optom Physiol Opt, Sept 1982;59(9):735.

CHAPTER 2

Organizational Years
1922–1929

I n spite of all the discussion for nearly twenty years about formation of a national academy of optometry, and several energetic attempts to do so, only a few small local academies were functioning by the early 1920s. Strangely enough, when the American Academy of Optometry was founded, it was done by a group of optometrists who, at least as far as the extant records show, had taken little part in any of the commotion about forming academies, or played any significant role in national optometric organizations or optometric education.

The organizational meeting was described in the press as follows:[1]

Paducah, Ky. Jan. 21. At a meeting held at the Planters Hotel in St. Louis, Jan. 11, an organization was formed for optometric study in higher branches, and for the exchange of ideas in optometric work. The organization, which will be known as the American Academy of Optometry, will also endeavor to establish standards of examination and practice among its members, and a code of professional ethics.

The next meeting will be held in Indianapolis, in June, at the time of the annual meeting of the A.O.A.

Those present were: Lee H. Tully, Evansville, Ind.; Dean S. Truax, Wichita, Kan.; William B. Irvine, Springfield, Ill.; T.M. Howe, Louisville, Ky.; C.S. Brown, Richmond, Mo.; W.A. Zeitler, St. Louis, Mo.; A.S. Hendrick, Lexington, Ky.; R.L. Searfoss, Odessa, Mo.; E.H. Schmidt, Washington, Mo.; C.F. Shepard, Hannibal, Mo.; M. Steinfeld, Paducah, Ky. *

M. Steinfeld, Paducah, Ky., was elected director of the organization until the next meeting in June. Optometrists who

---

* Lee H. Tully and W.A. Zeitler were medical doctors and were actively involved for the first few years.

are interested in higher education, and the other purposes of the organization are invited to write to the director or to any of the members. *

The eleven men who attended that meeting were all from cities within a few hundred miles of St. Louis. It is possible they had been meeting as a "study group," or at least knew each other, and had a common interest in advancing optometric education. M. Steinfeld, an optometrist from Paducah, Kentucky, "was responsible for the meeting and had invited certain of his friends to meet with him."[2]

That first meeting was purely organizational. The group decided to form a national academy. Some of the general matters of establishing an academy were discussed, along with various requirements for membership. Steinfeld was elected temporary chairman, which suggests he truly was the "founder." (It certainly is typical that the person with the idea gets elected chairman.) It was decided to meet again in June right after the AOA Congress in Indianapolis.

On June 29, 1922 a permanent organization was formed. M. Steinfeld, Paducah, Kentucky, was elected chairman; C.S. Brown, Richmond, Missouri, vice-chairman; and C.C. Koch, Minneapolis, Minnesota, secretary and treasurer. In addition to the above, the following men were made charter members with fellowships offered to each: R.L. Searfoss, Odessa, Missouri; L.L. DeMars, Minneapolis, Minnesota; S.H. Robinson, Prescott, Arizona; W.B. Irvine, Springfield, Illinois; T.M. Howe, Louisville, Kentucky; L.H. Tully, Evansville, Indiana; D. Truax, Wichita, Kansas; J.I. Kurtz, Minneapolis, Minnesota; W.A. Zeitler, St. Louis, Missouri; E. Schmidt, Washington, Missouri.

As secretary, Koch sent a bulletin to the membership soon after the meeting which described the nature of the organization:[3]

> This organization was not formed to take the place of the American Optometric Association, but is rather an organization formed to do research work along purely optometric lines. It has no political aspirations. Its intent being to work with the American Optometric Association, in the earnest effort to

---

* It is most likely that those attending the first organizational meeting were encouraged to do so by some of the individuals who had attempted to form academies previously — possibly E. LeRoy Ryer and Eugene Wiseman. Carel Koch in an interview once said Charles Sheard was involved but there is no other evidence of this. Ryer and Sheard became members of the Executive Council in December 1922 and Wiseman became president in December 1923. However, Steinfeld deserves the credit for taking the positive action that led to formation of the Academy.

better the educational standings of the men now practicing optometry.

Optometrists of high character and high standing throughout the country will be invited to join, and upon passing certain rigid qualification tests will be admitted to fellowship.

The Academy will meet at least once a year and probably twice, for its educational sessions. These meetings will be held at various centrally located cities. The next meeting is to be held in December of this year in St. Louis, Mo.

To assist the officers in getting the organization started, an assessment of $5 has been levied. This will carry us along until the December meeting, when the exact amount of yearly charges will be decided upon.

If you have not already done so, kindly send your check to your secretary-treasurer, who would also be glad to receive any suggestions you may have pertinent to the American Academy of Optometry.

The meeting in St. Louis, December 9–13, 1922, was the first at which papers were presented; thus it was the First Annual Meeting of the American Academy of Optometry. There were ten people present and the following subjects were presented: C.S. Brown, Astigmatism; E.E. Fielding, Anisometropia; L. Geiger, Retinoscopy; A.C. Hoffman, Paralysis of the Extrinsic Muscles; C.C. Koch, Importance of Taking a Case History; R.I. Searfoss, A Suggested Procedure in the Practice of Optometry; M. Steinfeld, Making an Optometric Diagnosis; P.H. Howard and W.A. Zeitler, Focal Infection and the Use of the Violet Ray.

There were several luncheons and dinners along with the usual speeches; one by past AOA President Oliver Abel of St. Louis. The final evening was called the Academy Round Table Dinner, held at the Chase Hotel, and it was reported that the stories told "would long live in the memories of those who heard them."[4] There was a short business meeting with the same officers reelected with E.E. Fielding added as treasurer. Though he was not present and apparently had no involvement up to this point, Eugene G. Wiseman, the same person who attempted to found the National Academy of Optometry in 1912, was appointed chairman of a committee to draw up a code of ethics. A three-man council was also appointed to "sit on all important acts of the Academy and assist the officers in passing on applicants for fellowship." Ernest Petry, Charles Sheard and E. LeRoy Ryer were named to this council for 1923.

There were forty members who received certificates at that time, and who thus are the charter members of the Academy. These men simply had been "approved" by the officers, and submitted no papers nor took any examination. The membership now included some educators, G.W. McFatrich, W.B. Needles, Charles Sheard, and A.P. DeKyper, along with A.J. Cross; but in general the Academy was operated by a group of practitioners.

An editorial in the optometric press praised the "good work of the Academy" and made some interesting comments reflecting some feelings of the time:[5]

> The criticism may be offered, however, that there is no real need for a special organization of optometrists to carry on the work outlined for this organization. Is not its existence in itself an implied reflection on the established A.O.A. organization and a danger to its unity? These are questions worth considering but we will not attempt at this time to do any more than briefly to refer to their significance. Educational work has been, from the beginning, one of the fundamental purposes of the national association, as well as of its affiliated State, provincial and local associations. We have State and national conventions that are intended to be, at least in part, educational.
>
> As to the strictly educational work of the Academy, so well started in St. Louis, it seems to us that it could well be brought within the fold of the national association, which could organize several Academies in various parts of the country, if it seemed desirable. There is quite evidently a growing demand for co-operative educational work for the men now in practice, work that they carry on themselves in their own way, with opportunities for mutual improvement by occasional meetings when they will hear serious and original papers read by their own members on subjects of practical concern, bearing on the every day practice of their profession.
>
> Whatever opinions may be entertained of the new organization, in reference to the other matter mentioned, it seems to us that it has set an excellent example in carrying on the exact kind of work of an educational and practical character that we have mentioned, and the members are entitled to congratulations for so doing. We believe that this kind of work will grow, whatever form of organization may be utilized for the purpose.

The constitution and bylaws of the Academy were published in *The Optical Journal and Review of Optometry* on February 8, 1923, though the Academy Transactions do not mention their presentation or adoption at the St. Louis meeting, nor does the record show presentation to the membership until the June 1924 meeting in Kansas City. * At that time it was called the "new" constitution and bylaws, and it does differ slightly from the original.

The object of the Academy was stated as follows: "To unite optometrists of recognized professional ability and ethical standing for the purpose of affording them opportunities of educational advancement; to establish a standard of optometric practice; to encourage and assist optometric research; and to work along all lines to raise the standards of optometric practice, education and ethics." Fundamentally its purpose is the same today with interest in research added. Interestingly, in 1924, members were all required to "in some way be identified with research."[6]

The Second Annual Meeting was held in Rochester, New York on December 10–11, 1923. Only five members were present and so no papers were presented, although several written papers had been submitted. The main item of business was the adoption of a code of ethics. All members of the Academy were put on probation for a period of three years relative to display advertising, during which time they could make whatever changes were necessary in their practices to conform to this ruling and five years relative to changing from store to office were designated. E.G. Wiseman was elected chairman of the Academy, and H. Bestor, vice chairman. C.C. Koch was reelected secretary, and E.E. Fielding, now of Omaha, Nebraska was reelected treasurer.

Initially, the three basic requirements for membership in the Academy were: (1) The candidate must practice in an office; (2) he must charge an examination fee of three dollars or more; and (3) he must not engage in advertising as in window displays, blotters, billboards, handbills, or even newspaper advertising. While these requirements may seem quite elementary by later standards, they were considerably ahead of the average practice of optometry as conducted in the early 1920s.[7]

There seems little doubt that one reason some optometrists were in favor of the Academy was because they were dissatisfied because the AOA did not require adherence to a strict code of ethics for membership. Ironically, over sixty years later, the federal government challenged restrictions on the mode of practice.

---

* See the Appendix for a copy of the first constitution and bylaws.

Probably because the attendance was so poor at the December meeting in 1923, the Third Annual Meeting was held in June 1924 at the same time as the AOA Convention. That did not help much even though attendance more than doubled to a total of thirteen. Only one paper was presented and a small amount of business was conducted.

A meeting was scheduled for December 1924 in Columbus but this was cancelled when it became apparent attendance would be very poor. It was intended to meet twice a year but it soon became obvious that would be too often. The next one was held in Buffalo, December 13-14, 1925. The record does not show how many were in attendance, though some papers were presented. The meeting was characterized by a few notes in the published report:[8]

> The banquet was held in the George Washington room of the Hotel Touraine. Mr. John McF. Howie delivered the address of the evening in his usual vigorous manner, comparing our constitution with that of our country and advocating strict adherence to the principles and precepts of each.
>
> The occasion was formal in every particular, and in general was in keeping with the superior grade of membership maintained by the Academy. It was highly creditable to our profession and significant of the possibilities when altruistic men gather together.
>
> This was true of the entire convention. It was a purely educational affair. The amount of time devoted to business affairs was less than an hour. There was no electioneering — no self-seeking of any kind other than the search for knowledge.
>
> While the discussion sometimes became rather heated, it was the fire generated by opinion conflicting with reference to scientific procedure and interpretations. This was beneficial as it brought out discussion which was much freer than it might have otherwise been. It was never personal or unpleasant. *

In an address at the meeting, Chairman Eugene G. Wiseman described what he saw at least as some of the reasons for formation of the

---

* The "heated" discussions following presentation of scientific papers was of great value in the minds of many participants. Not only did the discussions challenge the researchers and stimulate thinking, they were actually enjoyed by most participants. That was not true of all however. One past president tells of the caustic comments made to one lecturer about his methods and results, and as a result he never attended an Academy meeting again. There were no doubt a few others who could not stand the "heat."

Academy. His comments summarize, in a way, the situation in optometry at that time:[9]

> Something like five years ago it became evident to some that optometry was rapidly approaching a period when it would be necessary for the profession as a whole to adopt and proclaim a definite standard of practice below which one could not go and still be regarded as sincerely desirous of elevating our vocation to the professional level.
>
> Particularly in our national organization has it been evident that no marked change for the better would take place for a long time. Our national meetings have almost invariably been accompanied by political clamor, factional fights and energetic self-seeking. The scientific spirit was most noted by its absence. While practically all of the men who have been officers in the AOA have been splendid gentlemen, a cross section will show that they have been most notable as optical business men — that they certainly did not rank high as optometric scientists.
>
> Now it is essentially true that our organizations are democratic in spirit and principle. Therefore, we as a whole chose, even tho we chose by passive toleration, a type of official who is typical of the whole, and a tenor of meeting which is harmonious with the average spirit. This is inevitable and analogous with the fact that a stream can rise no higher than its source. We therefore get only what we deserve and we should not whine when the mirror reflects a true condition with ourselves in the picture.
>
> Since progress proved so slow and valuable opportunities were lost and the time and effort spent at most meetings largely wasted, it became evident that if a reasonably ideal association with others was to be consummated there must be formed a group of selected practitioners whose ideals were harmonious.
>
> But, until the formation of the Academy, these men did not have available a group in which they could feel entirely at home and free to express themselves with the confidence that they were in harmony with those around them. There was no group with whom they could associate with the assurance that they could learn from each as well as perhaps instruct each other.
>
> They could not very well discuss fees with men who charged no fees. They could not speak of the requirements of publicity with men who blazened out in crass display advertisements.

They could not interchange ideas concerning the psychology of surroundings with men who conducted stores. They could not safely advance ideas and conclusions relative to their scientific work for fear "store" men would seize them and prostitute them so as to bring discredit upon optometry. They could not converse about technical subjects with even some of the best known and most prosperous optometrists in the country because they could not be sure that these men were either interested in or had the slightest idea of what they were speaking. And often, when their consultants went to distant cities, they could not refer them to a particular individual because they could not be sure of the particular type of practice and service of that individual.

The organization of the American Academy of Optometry helps to solve all of these problems.

He then discussed the requirements for Academy membership and went on to say:

Hence, these requirements. They are higher than any other optometric organization has ever required. They may be too high. Time will tell but we are very confident that there are enough men in the country who can comply with them and who wish to be associated with such a group to make the Academy a power as long as optometry shall last.

In conclusion let me emphatically state this: All should thoroughly understand that while we disapprove of the atmosphere surrounding the usual optometric convention we are not in opposition to any other optometric association. In the Academy we seek for those things which we have been unable to find elsewhere and in it we endeavor to avoid some other things too commonly found in other gatherings. But we believe that these other gatherings serve an important purpose, that they should continue, and that Academy members should contribute to their success to any reasonable extent within their power.

Beginning in 1927, the transactions of the Academy were published by the Academy itself. The first volume included the meetings held in 1924 and 1925. In addition to a brief report of the business activities, the published volume — slightly over 100 pages — included papers on a variety of subjects, some having been presented at the meetings and others not. Thus, the Academy was providing education in printed form

PRESIDENTS OF THE
AMERICAN ACADEMY OF OPTOMETRY

MORRIS STEINFELD
1922–1923

EUGENE G. WISEMAN
1924–1928

BRIGGS S. PALMER
1930

as well as the presentations at the Academy meetings. There are thirteen volumes in all, covering fifteen annual meetings and a historical report of the two organizational meetings and the first annual meeting. Beginning with the meeting in 1940, the transactions were incorporated into the *American Journal of Optometry* and separate books of the transactions were not published.

The Fifth Annual Meeting was held in Washington, D.C., December 6–7, 1926. The members were very proud of the fact that the United States Bureau of Standards had invited the group to meet for one day at the bureau's building. Several of the lecturers were from the bureau and discussed testing glasses for protecting eyes from injury and the properties of safety goggles. This was the first time scientists who were not optometrists or physicians appeared on the program. There was also a trip through the bureau's facilities. Business affairs were at a minimum, in fact only thirty minutes were scheduled for business. The same officers were reelected for the next year, and thus Wiseman began his fourth term in 1927.

Wiseman could not resist the temptation to push for more members, though he did not say "Wanted: 1000 men," as he had when trying to start the National Academy fifteen years before. He wrote an article to bring the Academy to the attention of more optometrists and included word for word the address given at the 1925 meeting:[10]

> No fanfare of trumpets nor radio roar greeted the birth of this "young hopeful," nor has there been any broadcasting to popularize it or greatly to swell its membership. Its organizers were content to let the Academy *idea* grow by natural accretion. They did not want to create artificial interest or demand, for they knew, from previous history and experience, that interest stimulated by high pressure methods soon subsides. The Academy is not seeking a large membership — indeed, its requirements preclude any such possibility — but its officials believe that those practitioners who have vainly sought association with men and women similarly minded ought to know that an organization of such has been effected and is functioning.

That appeal must have done some good, at least the attendance at the 1927 meeting, December 4–6 in New York City, was large enough that eight papers were presented, including ones by Professors J.P.C. Southall, R.B. Raup and Frederic A. Woll, from Columbia University. There were several luncheons and a banquet where several informal addresses were delivered. The business meeting included the recommendation that the *American Journal of Optometry* be designated as the official organ of the Academy. * Particularly significant was the proposal that a research fellowship in optometry be established at Columbia University, which was carried out the following year.

The *American Journal of Optometry* each month published a number of scientific articles. It was the official journal for eight states, mostly in the mid-west. Its editor was Carel C. Koch, who was also active in the Academy, presently on its Executive Council. In the September 1927 issue there was an editorial by LeRoy Ryer. [11] He stated there was need for both the AOA and AAO, maintaining that the AOA must play a role in politics and that because of that, education could not be given adequate attention. He explained that a number of men were active in both organizations. Most important, he urged all local academies to enlist under the American Academy and to attend its meetings.

The following month, Koch himself editorialized about the academy. [12] He mentioned several interesting suggestions that had been made about Academy activities. One was that the Academy establish a commission to pass upon new refractive appliances which were constantly being submitted to the profession and to also pass upon and grade the various types of material offered to the profession by the optical manufacturers. This was thought to be extremely important and it was said that the Academy could have the assistance of the technical laboratory staffs of two large universities, as well as the technical training of the members of the commission themselves, to call upon in examining the material or equipment, and verifying the statements and claims of the makers.

Another proposed activity was the building up of an optometric library at one of the "larger" optometric schools. This library was intended to form a permanent archives for optometric literature, with a librarian whose duty it would be to file papers, manuscripts and books and properly index them. The profession needed some sort of archives where at least one copy of each piece of printed material would be kept on file, Koch said.

The greater attention the Academy was receiving did result in a good increase in membership, the total reaching seventy-four in 1928 and 108 in 1929. The numbers attending the annual meeting also rose with twenty-five at the Chicago meeting and forty-one in Boston the following year. The meeting program in 1928 listed seventeen papers to be

---

* The term *Academy Journal* or simply the *Journal* is used throughout this book for convenience. Its history is described in the Appendix.

presented, among them were two by individuals who played very significant roles in optometry. Charles Sheard, at that time with the Mayo Clinic, spoke on the subject "Is There a Zone of Ocular Comfort?"* A.M. Skeffington presented a paper entitled: "Remote Ophthalmoscopic Diagnosis."** Skeffington was also elected to the Academy Executive Council though he only served two years.

Two major changes in leadership took place at the end of the 1920s. Carel Koch became chairman in 1929, replacing Eugene Wiseman who had been such a dominant figure for all of the Academy's early years. He probably had more to do with its character and development to this point than anyone else. This also marked the beginning of the career of J. Fred Andreae as secretary in 1928, a position he was to hold for seventeen years. He became president of the American Optometric Association (1930–1932) and president of the Academy in 1945. Thus Andreae was also a major influence on the development of the Academy. Koch of course had been secretary or on the Executive Council from the very beginning but he no longer was an officer or Executive Council member after his chairmanship in 1929 until he returned in 1945 to follow Andreae as secretary, and to hold that position for the next 29 years. Serving also as editor of its journal from 1924 until 1968, Koch was the most predominant single person in Academy history.

Up to this period, little information about Academy activities between annual meetings appeared in print. No doubt the chairman and the secretary were occupied with business matters and correspondence. Dues were collected and expenses covered as reported each year by the secretary-treasurer. In 1928 with Volume Five, the *American Journal of Optometry* became the official news organ of the Academy.[13] However, there was very little news about the Academy. Papers read at the annual meeting were still published separately. Since the educational program was the principal work of the Academy, there was little other activity between times other than maintaining the organization and arranging the annual meeting.

There is some evidence of activity between annual meetings in 1929. Chairman Koch gave a rather extensive report at the Eighth Annual Meeting in Boston, December 15–18, accounting for other activities of the Academy. Some were detailed as follows:[14]

---

* Charles Sheard was the founder of the course in applied optics at Ohio State University in 1914 that developed into the present-day College of Optometry.
** A.M. Skeffington was the director of education of the Optometric Extension Program, a lecturer on its programs, and author of many of its published papers for nearly fifty years.

In January of this year the Executive Council of the Academy decided to incorporate our body so as to protect the name and also to enable the Academy to issue charters to local Academies, retaining at the same time the power of revoking these sub-charters should this become necessary at any time. We felt at that time, that the only way to have absolute control of the Academy situation was by incorporating, and so during the past year this was done.

Our Academy is incorporated under the laws of the District of Columbia, an official seal has been drawn up and the machinery for local Academies is now underway. In fact, at this meeting, we expect to issue a number of local charters to various fellows of the American Academy of Optometry.

Regarding the local charters let me say that we are in no way desirous of duplicating State Associations in any way whatsoever. The local Academy of Optometry, it must be understood is not to be organized for defensive purposes nor is it to in any way rival State Associations now in existence. In fact, members of local Academies should at all times belong to and be active in their State Association work. I wish to be emphatic in my statement of this at this time because there has been some criticism of the Academy by certain A.O.A. officials who felt we were perhaps attempting to duplicate the efforts of the A.O.A. along this line. Nothing is further from the truth. It is my firm conviction and in this the Executive Council concurs.

In January I created three technical committees, the first of these was a Committee on New Instruments and Techniques. This committee was to make a study of various new apparatus and report its findings back to the American Academy of Optometry at this meeting. To enable members of this committee to get together and to meet at least several times during the year, I appointed on this committee only men and women from Massachusetts. In other words, what is now the local Academy from Massachusetts, was given, under the direction of W.I. Brown, the assignment of studying new instruments and techniques with the request that they report their findings at this meeting in Boston.

The second committee which was appointed with Elmer E. Hotaling as its chairman, was a committee to study the *Effects of Eliminating Certain Portions of The Spectrum by Means of Calobar Glass in Certain Cases of Senile Opacity.* In this instance various members throughout the United States were appointed to this committee, each member receiving certain blanks which should be filled out with a specific date, these to be mailed to Chairman Hotaling, who is conducting a series of elaborate researches in New York City and the report of his findings will be presented before this body during this meeting.

The third technical committee was a committee to study the effects of certain forms of *Physical Therapy Upon the Eye*. This committee was headed by J.I. Kurtz who will also deliver a report during our sessions in Boston.

As I have said before, the Chairmen have not perhaps received the fullest support by various members of their committees and this is believed due to the newness of the plan. As far as I know this is an initial attempt to do technical work by means of committees in offices of the practitioners themselves, but I am convinced that with the proper handling over several years of time that a number of worthwhile projects can be started and a tremendous amount of interest can be aroused in this form of Academy work which can be carried on during twelve months of each year under the direction of the American Academy of Optometry through perhaps the local Academies, the work itself being done by individual members collaborating together.

In January of this year a committee of New York men headed by E. LeRoy Ryer was appointed by your Chairman to study the advisability of inaugurating a research fellowship at Columbia University. After some discussion with various authorities, it was decided to hold the matter in abeyance until the following year. After some correspondence with our Executive Council, your chairman decided that it was idle to gather and talk about this matter without knowing definitely whether or not the money could be raised to successfully launch such a project should it be so desired, and with this in mind, he determined during the fall of this year to sound out the reactions of our various members to determine whether or not a sufficient number was interested to make this plan feasible. If the money could be raised, then all that was necessary when we meet in Boston was to decide whether or not to establish this research fellowship. On the other hand, obviously, if the money could not be raised, we could all save time by not talking about the matter at all. During the months of August, September and October a rather vigorous campaign was carried on from your Chairman's office. A large number of letters being sent out with the result that one-third of the members of the Academy pledged $1,440 for the research fellowship fund. While this amount is not as large as had been hoped for, it nevertheless places the goal well within our reach and should the incoming administration wish to carry on this matter, it can now easily do so.

The 1929 meeting was an extensive one and included a trip to the plant of the American Optical Company. Briggs S. Palmer was elected chairman for 1930. He had been president of the AOA from 1906 through 1908. The papers presented covered a variety of topics from "Iridology" to "The Application of Telescopic Spectacles in Refraction," by William Feinbloom, the first presentation relating to subnormal vision. Viewed from present-day knowledge some of the papers may seem rudimentary, perhaps some not highly scientific. But the Academy was only eight years old and the knowledge of optometric science was in its infancy at the time. The very purpose of the Academy was to provide a forum for exchange of ideas and an opportunity to improve quality.

More optometric educators were becoming Academy members and more scientists from outside optometry were making presentations. Stature of the annual meeting was improving and quality of the papers presented and those published in the *American Journal of Optometry* were achieving higher standards. But apparently the concept that each member must be "related to research" was being ignored. The Academy was very concerned about research and the plan to establish a research fellowship was pressed forward. The development of the idea that one be established at Columbia University, and the work that was done to bring this about, was described in the *American Journal of Optometry* in November, 1930. The establishment of the fellowship was announced as follows:[15]

> After much conferring, the man selected was Dr. Wm. Feinbloom of Brooklyn. Dr. Feinbloom is a graduate of Columbia and has had several years of practice and is keenly interested in the scientific side of Optometry. He has displayed marked ability in research work and brings to his new task a most refreshing enthusiasm. He is an Academy member, a fact which had no particular bearing upon his selection, but one which must be gratifying to Academy members. No move has been made in this project without a great deal of deliberation. We believe that this is one of optometry's greatest opportunities

to demonstrate its genuine desire to promote scientific research and we wanted to make no mistakes.

But even though the Academy was progressing, and its nature becoming more clearly determined, there were still some optometrists who were dubious about its need and purpose. This is evident from the following letter:

Boston, Mass. Jan. 20, 1930

Editor, The Optical Journal-Review:

After the very interesting and enlightening session of the American Academy of Optometry, recently held in Boston, it came to my attention that some optometrists think the Academy members are a "holier than thou" group or, in the terminology of Professor Rogers of the Massachusetts Institute of Technology, "Optometric Snobs." It is to dispel any and all erroneous ideas regarding the Academy that I ask for a little of your valuable space.

Stated in the clearest words at my command, I can say the Academy stands for the *highest and best in optometric practice.* It desires to draw into its membership every optometrist who puts service to the patient above everything else; who is constantly striving to render better service; who by his personal as well as professional life and conduct, shows that he realizes that optometry will receive only that recognition and respect to which he is entitled.

A member must conduct his or her practice as an office practice and not as a store. A fee must be charged consistent with the service rendered and in accordance with the practice of the best optometrists in the community. Advertising in newspapers, on bill boards, or with blotters, novelties, handbills, etc., cannot be indulged in. Membership is by invitation from some member of the Academy.

It remains, then for all who wish to advance the cause of optometry to become proficient by earnest study and conscientious practice, and this is what the Academy is fostering.

It is my hope that the many optometrists all over the country who are qualified to meet these very reasonable requirements will be asked to join and will accept. They need the Academy and the Academy needs them.

The Academy is in no way antagonistic to any other optometric organization. Its one great objective is to build optometry into a profession which will take the high place it is entitled to hold, and be of inestimable value to suffering humanity.

Briggs S. Palmer,
Chairman, American Academy
of Optometry

By no means did that put the issue to rest. The years ahead would continue to be filled with uncertainty and misunderstanding about the relationships between the AAO and the AOA. But the Academy was moving ahead. The next decade would produce significant harmony between the two organizations to the benefit of the profession and the organizations themselves.

REFERENCES

1. American Academy of Optometry organized for educational work. Opt J Rev Optom, Jan 26, 1922;49(3):39.
2. Trans AAO 1926;1:13. *
3. Bulletin for entire membership American Academy of Optometry. Optom Wkly, Aug 3, 1922;50(5):46.
4. Trans AAO 1926;1:14.
5. Good work of the Academy. Opt J Rev Optom, Dec 21, 1922;50(26):27-28.
6. Ibid p. 16.
7. Hirsch MJ, Wick RE. The Optometric Profession. Philadelphia: Chilton Press, 1968:153.
8. Trans AAO 1926;1:65.
9. Ibid pp. 6-12.
10. Wiseman EG. The American Academy of Optometry. Optom Wkly, Oct 13, 1927;18(32):1139-1140.
11. Ryer EL. The American Academy of Optometry and the AOA. Am J Optom, Sept 1927;4(9):275-277.
12. Koch CC. The Academy and its work. Am J Optom, Oct 1927;4(10):315-316.
13. Hirsch MJ, Weiner G. History of the American Journal of Optometry. Am J Optom Arch Am Acad Optom, Jan 1968;45(1):44.

* References to Academy activities reported as "Transactions" of the Academy will be referred to for convenience as Transactions of the AAO. Thirteen volumes were published by the Academy covering the fourth through the eighteenth annual meeting, the first in 1927 and the last in 1940. They were titled Report of the Transactions of the Annual Meeting. There is a complete set in the AAO Archives, ILAMO, St. Louis.

At the time of the fourth annual meeting in December 1925, the secretary, Carel C. Koch, gave a report of the first three meetings. Thus references to all of them in the Transactions are in Volume I, published in 1927.

In 1941 the American Journal of Optometry began publishing the Transactions of the Academy and the publication became known as the American Journal of Optometry and the Archives of American Academy of Optometry. From then on, the various items generally carried titles and they are so referenced when a meaningful title was designated.

14. Chairman's address. Trans AAO, Nov 1930;4:14-16.
15. Fellowship of the American Academy of Optometry established at Columbia University. Am J Optom, Nov 1930;7(11):621-623.

CHAPTER 3

The Expanding
Role of the Academy
1930–1939

I t is probable that in the year 1930 the American Academy of Optometry had "arrived," and would not "fade away," as one writer had characterized other academies. By no means were its troubles over, and certainly few, if any, optometrists would bet that it would be healthy and strong a decade hence. Still it had survived for eight years, the last three of them beginning a time of promising growth. It certainly seemed reasonably certain that there was enough interest in this type of organization that energies could be devoted to more than just staying alive.

Membership reached 134, a number not to be exceeded for another six years when it began to slowly increase again. Still thirty to forty members attended the annual meetings, and as might be expected, it was the same small group of individuals who came and presented papers. They did so at their own expense, and the fact that they persisted illustrates their true dedication to the concept of the Academy.

The large majority of the membership never attended a meeting. Presumably they received the *American Journal of Optometry* as part of their dues, and it carried some educational articles. They also received a copy of the yearly publication *The Academy Transactions*, which included papers presented at the annual meetings. Beyond that, the benefits were purely in the self-satisfaction of belonging to a scientific body with high standards, and perhaps in "supporting the cause."

Certainly the Academy was not involved, officially at least, in politics. In fact it had no activities other than the annual meeting, limited support of research, and publishing the *Transactions*. In what other ways it should function was most uncertain, but it had reached a point where it was healthy enough to consider — and attempt — some other activities.

35

This led to controversy. That was nothing new because, from the time of the proposal of an academy in 1905 by LeRoy Ryer, there was constant discussion about why have two such organizations — AOA and AAO. The burning issue was the matter of professionalism and commercialism. Aside from the question of creating a scientific body and upgrading education, the matter of ethical standards caused the greatest emotion and the most rhetoric.

It is not that the AOA was unconcerned with ethics and professionalism. In its early life it attacked other problems first, passage of laws regulating optometry being the most vital. Later, in the 1950s, the matter of a code of practice became critical for the AOA. Both organizations, AOA and the Academy, had rules that limited membership to individuals who adhered to certain standards. Though it has been stated here before, and will be again, how ironic it is that fifty years later the AOA essentially has open membership, while the emphasis in the Academy has shifted from matters of concern about office appearance and advertising to a high level of competence, knowledge, and dedication to continued learning.

An article entitled "The American Academy of Optometry" by E. LeRoy Ryer and E.E. Hotaling, published in May 1930, stated that the Academy would be the salvation of optometry, not because it was an educational and scientific body, but because it would guide the profession out of commercialism:[1]

> Optometry has come to a fork in the road. Destiny insists she go on. But to go on involves a most critical choice, *i.e.,* shall she take the commercial way or the professional? One may lead to ultimate ruin — one to success. One is the wrong road — one the right road. * Which shall it be? Can she not continue to hide behind sophistry, hypocrisy and sham? Can she not continue to pose as professional and *be* commercial? Is there no way to garner the best each has to offer and thus avoid making the choice? Though no other ever so stood, cannot this house stand divided against itself? Cannot it remain half commercial and half professional?
>
> The American Academy of Optometry lifts its eyes from the

---

* Optometry it seems has always been and still is, at the "crossroads," that very term being used in the titles of articles and speeches many times, and, as recent as 1985, the term "crisis in optometry" was used. Fortunately the profession has apparently always made a wise choice as to which road to take and no doubt the Academy has been a significant factor in making the decisions.

ruts, sees a glowing promise down the professional road, accepts responsibility of leadership along that road, charts its course on hard-headed, common sense professional principles and calls every professional-minded optometrist to its colors.

Our latest danger lurks in the possibility of her choosing to build upon commercial instead of professional principles, and therein lies the most serious problem optometry ever faced. It has been a chronic problem for years; it is now acute. It should be met squarely.

After expanding the various reasons the public would get better vision care in a professional setting, the authors pointed out that the public is becoming enlightened and will not "buy" glasses in stores, and that the Academy will be an effective force in helping the professionally minded optometrist:

> The American Academy of Optometry is dedicated to the advancement of this group and to the establishment of professional ideals and principles.
>
> The will to serve must be the cornerstone of any profession and the academy asks its fellows to think, and act in terms of serving rather than of selling, not only as a worthy ideal but also as the only sensible course.
>
> But the will to serve, if it is to be effective must embody the power to serve and the American Academy of Optometry by every means at its command aims to place in the hands of every optometrist willing and able to receive it the power to serve humanity, to guard its ocular welfare.
>
> Toward this end the American Academy of Optometry is establishing fellowships; instituting investigations along any line promising new, usable data; presenting the results of the work of any of its fellows not only to all its fellows at stated meetings but to all interested through publications in appropriate magazines; by supporting magazines which champion modern professional practice; by co-operating with the professional schools teaching optometry; and by helping graduates of these schools attain and retain professional standards.
>
> Such aims demand and warrant strict insistence upon professional standards and, obviously cannot avoid deprecating the old, venerable but outworn commercial practices that have not only held back optometry, hurt the optical industry, but have kept the patient from getting fair treatment.

The authors' strong plea for professionalism stressed the fact that the public would be better served by it. But it too was a plea for joining the Academy. Here is how they stated the case:

> We have shown why a distinction must be drawn between those who would keep optometry a small, insignificant slow-turnover business and those who would see it develop into a highly specialized, broadly-useful, widely-respected profession. We have shown what constitutes a professional-minded practitioner. And we have shown why the American Academy of Optometry must insist upon strict professional practice.
>
> Who is eligible to fellowship in the American Academy of Optometry?
>
> Anyone who, seeing beyond his nose, realizes that optometry must develop professionalward or die.
>
> Anyone who sees that the true value of glasses and of eye work can never be established so long as either is offered as merchandise in stores.
>
> Anyone who, realizing the responsibility that lies back of safeguarding human vision, is willing to prepare himself inwardly and outwardly to meet that responsibility competently and honorably.
>
> Anyone who, thinking of his own eyes or his child's eyes or the eyes of any of his loved ones, has grit enough to say that commercial methods cannot guarantee the care he would demand.
>
> Anyone who sees the eyes of the world not a field for exploitation but a field which holds out generous rewards to him who will serve unselfishly.
>
> Anyone who takes optometry seriously.

No doubt Ryer and Hotaling's article expressed the feelings of most of the Academy membership. This somewhat picturesque and fiery language may have offended a few — though it was rather typical of their time — but the points they made certainly well described the status of optometry. It is easy to imagine that the implication that the AAO would save the profession did not set well with some leaders of the AOA — even though the Academy continually expressed the point that it had no quarrel with AOA.* In 1966 the *Journal of the American Optometric Association* dedicated most of its October issue to the Academy. Its editorial was entitled: "The American Academy of Optometry; Vehicle for Education and Ethics," showing that, ultimately, the organizations learned to get along with each other.

The activity of the Academy in other areas was described in the address of Chairman Briggs S. Palmer at the ninth annual meeting in Omaha, Nebraska, December 13–15, 1930. Palmer had been president of the AOA from 1906 to 1908, yet here, as Academy chairman, he was proposing actions that might have been considered more appropriate for the AOA:[2]

> This Academy stands for strictly professional optometry. Its efforts to bring this about are greatly hampered by the large number of optometrists who do not practice professionally. This lowers the standing of optometry in the minds of the public. One of the biggest problems before us today is to find some way to make practicing optometry attractive and financially desirable for those now practicing and make it possible for every graduate from our colleges to follow the ideas and ideals that make for success. I believe we should appoint committees of our Fellows, residing in or near the cities where the colleges of optometry are located. These committees should learn who the graduates are to be, all about their plans for the future and in every way possible, act as advisors and helpers to these graduates. They need help and we must help them. If we can thus look after the graduate and assist him in establishing a professional practice and then bring those now practicing to see the value of a professional practice without causing them to suffer a financial loss, we will indeed be building a strong professional optometry. We must set ourselves to this vital problem and find a solution.
>
> Another matter that demands our attention is the value of, and the need for, Fellows of this Academy who are capable of addressing public gatherings of layman and present optometry's

---

* Though perhaps many optometrists had no quarrel with the AOA, they felt it was not moving fast enough, a statement which has been true to some degree at any time in history. These comments are not meant to be critical of the AOA, only to state opinions that existed at the time.

view from a "human interest" viewpoint. If we can have the
right men and the required financial backing, much good can
be done for optometry.

Establishing graduates in successful practices and public education
are still priorities in the 1980s with optometric organizations. The fact
that these projects were proposed in 1930 shows that the Academy not
only had recognized them, but had reached the strength in numbers and
had acquired adequate funds to be able to consider more than the
annual meetings and publication of papers. But in addition to these
proposed projects, several important activities had taken place.

The research fellowship had been established at Columbia University, and William Feinbloom had started a project dealing with
strabismus. The year before, it had been decided to establish local
academies as affiliates. This had been quite effective, and it was
announced in 1930 that seven had been instituted in the areas of
Washington, D.C., and Baltimore; Minneapolis; New York City; De-
troit; Omaha; Marion, Indiana; and Little Rock, Arkansas. *

There was a report of the Committee on Physical Agents. The
committee was investigating the merits of new instruments and techniques, and reported on preliminary work. An interesting name elected
to the executive council was that of E.B. Alexander of Duncan, Oklahoma. ** In attendance also was Ernest Kiekenapp, secretary of the
AOA, who became a very important figure in the profession. *** The
first resolution to be passed by the Academy, on record at least, is a
rather curious one. There is no comment in the record as to what
specific incidents raised this issue:[3]

> A resolution was presented and after some discussion was
> unanimously accepted as follows:
> *Whereas,* there appeared in certain optometrical profes-

---

* The history of the formation of the chapters of the Academy is rather unclear. The
records are not complete and some chapters were called by various names from time
to time. Some were active, then ceased and started up later. The Appendix
contains a brief history of the chapters based upon present-day records.

** E.B. Alexander was one of the founders of the Optometric Extension Program
(OEP) in 1928, and served as its president for many years. A past president stated
off the record that there was discussion of a merger of the Academy and the OEP if
Alexander became Academy chairman. However, he was on the executive council
only one year.

*** Kiekenapp was secretary of the AOA for 35 years. He also was the founder of the
Journal of the American Optometric Association and was its editor for 32 years. Thus,
his role with the AOA covered about the same time and the same activities as did
that of Carel Koch with the AAO.

PRESIDENTS OF THE
AMERICAN ACADEMY OF OPTOMETRY

WALTER I. BROWN
1931–1932

O.J. MELVIN
1933–1934

ROBERT N. WALKER
1935–1936

RICHARD M. HALL
1937–1938

sional publications some criticism of the policy of the American Academy of Optometry in following the usual scientific procedure of such bodies, by permitting the presentation of scientific and theoretic papers and,

Whereas, The American Academy of Optometry does stand and has always stood for the use of accepted and proved techniques in optometry, although inviting and providing for the presentation and democratic consideration of new ideas thought by their opponents to be relevant to optometry, and

Whereas, The American Academy in no way assumes responsibility for, or endorses in any way new ideas or techniques, therefore

Be It Resolved that The American Academy of Optometry goes on record as censuring those optometrical publications which accept and print such criticisms.

The Tenth Annual Meeting held in Philadelphia, December 6–8, 1931, was apparently rather unspectacular, with only eight papers presented as compared to eighteen the year before. Business transacted was very brief, even though a new constitution and bylaws with very few changes was adopted. However, the lectures produced some newspaper publicity. Of interest to the local press were items about such things as an imagined city twenty-five years hence with everything in restful shades of green; the possibility that twenty-five percent of motor accidents may be due to defective vision; and a warning that parents should not try to change children's handedness.[4] Academy members were quite likely glad to make the news even if the subject was a bit imaginative.

In spite of some sharp differences of opinion about the roles of the AAO and AOA, some individuals were active in both organizations, indeed some serving as leaders of both. Briggs S. Palmer, who was the Academy president in 1930 (one term), had been AOA president from 1906 to 1908 (two terms). In 1930, J. Fred Andreae became president of the AOA and served for two terms, though he had never been on the board of trustees or served as an officer before going directly to the presidency.[5] At the same time that he was serving as AOA president, he was the secretary-treasurer of the Academy, having begun his term in 1928. He later became president of the Academy for 1945 and 1946.

Walter I. Brown became chairman of the Academy in December 1930 for two terms, after having served on its executive council in 1929, but not in 1930. While still serving as chairman of the Academy, Brown became vice president of the AOA for two years, and then became president in 1934 for two terms.*

There was no regular succession through the chairs as became common later in both AOA and the Academy; thus there was less continuity of leadership. It would seem that Andreae's and Brown's presence in both AAO and AOA should have brought closer relations between the two organizations, and possibly it did so, since there is little evidence of friction in the next few years. Brown, in his address to the Eleventh Annual Meeting, spoke of attempts to develop "visual examination methods of a more uniform procedure" and described a foundation for this process. He also added that "now after two years we should advance rapidly and without friction with any optometric organization."[6]

Attendance at the 1932 meeting in Chicago totaled thirty-one. Membership had dropped to 118, and the secretary reported that dues collection had been slow, possibly because of the economic depression. Still, fifteen papers were presented, and a list of their topics provides an insight into the areas of practice receiving attention. The subjects were: "A Study of the Extrinsic Ocular Muscles," R.M. Hall, Cleveland, Ohio; "Refraction With and Without a Cycloplegic," J.I. Kurtz, Minneapolis, Minnesota; "Amblyopic Treatment Technics," Harry E. Pine, Chicago, Illinois; "Recognition of Ocular Pathology," D.R. Paine, Topeka, Kansas; "A Case Leading to a Study of the Accommodation-Convergence Relationship," L.K. Wyatt; "The Effects of Radiant Energy on Animal and Plant Tissues," Charles Sheard, Rochester, Minnesota; "Optical Control of the Central Gray," H. Riley Spitler, Eaton, Ohio; "Optometric Survey of Incorrigible Children in Chicago Parental School," W.B. Needles and W.J. Heather, Chicago, Illinois; "The New Sub-Normal Vision Lens," William Feinbloom, New York City; "The Art of Optometry," E. LeRoy Ryer, New York City; "Some Vital Economic Factors in Practice," O.J. Melvin, Omaha, Nebraska; "The Use of Visible Light in the Correction of Refractive and Muscular Abnormalities," Carel C. Koch, Minneapolis, Minnesota; "A Report on the Experimental Variation of the Stimulus Conditions in the Quantitative Determination of the Responses in the Accommodation-Convergence Reflex," Edwin Forbes Tait, Philadelphia, Pennsylvania; "A Case of Total Monolateral Blindness Treated Successfully With the Use of Physical Agents," J.I. Kurtz, Minneapolis, Minnesota; and "The Successful Treatment of a Case of Bilateral Ptosis," J.I. Kurtz.

The years 1933, 1934, and 1935 were similar to the previous two or

---

* Melvin Wolfberg also has been president of both AOA, 1969-1970 (one term), and AAO, 1985-1986 (two terms).

three years in many regards. The Academy was in a somewhat status quo posture. Membership and meeting attendance continued about the same; the programs were similar, and about the same people were involved. The officers concluded that the severe depression and the thrust of commercialism were reasons for no growth. One activity that did expand during the period was the instigation of fellowships for research at the 1932 annual meeting:[7]

> In accordance with the terms of a resolution approved at the 1932 meeting of the American Academy of Optometry, a limited number of Fellowships for Research are now offered by the Executive Council of that organization.
>
> These Fellowships are intended primarily to stimulate interest and productive work in optometry, physiological optics and their underlying sciences.
>
> To be eligible for appointment to an American Academy of Optometry Fellowship, the applicant must:
>
> 1. Hold a baccalaureate degree in arts and science from an accredited college or university;
> 2. Be a graduate in optometry from an accredited institution and eligible to practice in at least one state;
> 3. Have been actually enrolled for at least one year as a graduate student in the graduate school of a fully accredited university;
> 4. Have as his major subject physiological optics or one of the following underlying sciences: anatomy, physiology, physiological chemistry, pathology, psychology, or physics.
>
> American Academy of Optometry Fellowships for Research are usually awarded for one year but may be continued at the discretion of the Director of Research. The stipend is not fixed but varies according to the amount of time given to the research work of the Fellow. It averages $200 to $300 yearly, plus an additional allowance to cover the expense of equipment and the Fellow's appearance at the yearly meeting of the Academy.
>
> All applicants for research must be eligible to become members of the American Academy of Optometry and, if not already members, become such when their applications for Research Fellowships are approved.

The published transactions of the Academy during its early years are very brief. The other journals carried very few details of the business of the AAO, but there are no known records from its secretaries and officers in existence. It is difficult to determine, at least during this period, who the research fellows were or how they were selected. In fact, it is uncertain how applications for the Academy were approved. Apparently each applicant had to be sponsored by a member and submit a paper. However, there are no details about this. There is no doubt that each member must practice in a "professional environment" but beyond that there is no description as to what that environment was. From time to time there were comments to the effect that too many optometrists were not adhering to the ethical standards, but no specifics were stated.

There was concern that perhaps the meeting time in December was one of the reasons for poor attendance. The membership was polled and voted in favor of changing to the end of August. This resulted in nearly a fifty percent increase in attendance at the Fourteenth Annual Meeting in New York City, August 25–27, 1935. At that time the Committee of Investigation, chaired by O.J. Melvin, made a report on a point which apparently had begun to create some dissension:[8]

> There are two distinct groups in the Academy. One, the practicing optometrists, who financially support the work done by the research group. The other is the research group, who have been contributing most valuable research material, of which the Academy is justly proud. These two groups are of equal importance. Their value to optometry and its progress, as well as to the welfare of the Academy, is so well recognized, that further consideration at this time is unnecessary.
>
> The first group, the practicing optometrist, is a man who, because of the demands of his practice, personal inclination, or lack of facilities, finds it an impossibility to prepare or present to the Academy, anything which could be recognized as academic research material. Therefore, he has had a choice of submitting nothing to the Academy or, if he does submit something, to open himself to unfair discussion of his subject by the research men, which borders, in many cases, on ridicule.
>
> An attempt has been made this year to have such material presented to the Academy. There was considerable difficulty in getting men to participate, for the above-mentioned reasons. The presentation of such material by these men will do much to increase the interest of this group in the Academy activities, for, while this group is intensely interested in the progress of the research work, presented by the research fellows, in many instances, this work is little understood by the practicing group.

If the material is to be presented at the Academy meetings by practicing optometrists, the men doing academic research must decide once and for all, whether or not they can be interested in such material and can discuss it from the point of view of a practicing rather than an academic research man. Passive, amused dismissal of these papers will be just as destructive to their appearance, as unfair criticism. I am sure that the research fellows have never looked at it from this point of view, therefore, the existence of this condition is not to be construed as a criticism of them. *

Was the Academy becoming too academic for the practicing optometrist? Was it becoming primarily a forum for scientists to exchange information? Certainly more educators and researchers were becoming involved. Were other sources beginning to fill the need for education of the general practitioner? Some twenty years later the Academy would address this problem by establishing a continuing education program.

The reports of meetings and the addresses of officers often made it seem like a body such as the Academy was all work and no play. * * Yet there were always banquets and social events which provided good fellowship as well as education and knowledge exchange. The flavor of this aspect of AAO meetings comes through best in the descriptions of reporters from the optometric press. Not many of these exist but one appearing in the *Optometric Weekly*, August 27, 1936, touches on this aspect:[9]

> On Monday evening, August 24th, (1936 in Chicago) the Academy sat down to its annual banquet.
>
> It was a very friendly affair — almost a love feast. Those present enjoyed a fine dinner, spirits were high (eighth floor). The Academy is a scientific body, scientifically inclined. Bill Feinbloom was researching the last course — ice cream — which only Chicago could produce. The universal language of esperanto was introduced by Skeff who was nervously pacing up and down the floor. What we heard in part seemed to be pure English, but some of the words sounded as if they began with a

---

* At least in one instance a practitioner was so offended by the stout criticism by a researcher that he walked out of the room. O.J. Melvin apparently recognized there were two sides to this problem and that fairness should prevail.

* * The Academy was primarily scientific in its nature, not social, and it is not intended to imply otherwise. Yet there were certainly social and fellowship aspects and the various Academy officers and members interviewed for this book certainly stressed the value of this in exchanging ideas on a very informal basis.

capital "S." Poor Alex was spread out on two chairs for comfort — and batted one thousand. Every time he tried to speak, he was never recognized. The best authorities informed us that Melvin would be given ten years — the informer expected to be there in five, waiting for him. Professor Sheard enjoyed his meal with his coat off and promised, "Topaz, you'll get it."

At the distinguished table, our good friend Fred Andreae was nursing his arm, which, we understand, was broken on the train. And the beauteous Francis Marshall did not rise to the occasion.

Ezell, with his usual pleasant smile was one of the listeners. Bill Needles got it off his chest. Dewey was napping. The founders, Koch and Kurtz, demonstrated the actual spirit of the Academy. Professor Poser gave a pleasant discourse in abbreviated form. Ewalt agreed that scientists have a scientific mind. Fitch smiled and his propensity protruded. Doris Pine missed her children by staying over night at the hotel. The A.O.A. secretary, Kiekenapp, acted with his usual precision. Miss Grannis appeared in a ball gown. Farmer could hear well on necessity. Walker's dream to retire was realized. Titus's suit needed a little alteration. Hotaling considered it too long a time to be away from his wife, could scarcely wait for the five o'clock train. Jerome Heather is still a Democrat. Harry Pine let his unconscious speak. Seward took matters seriously. Good old Folsom was speechless. The California Clarks acknowledged the beauties of Chicago.

We thank you, American Academy, for your hospitality, appreciating it sincerely, and wish you every success for the future.

There was a notable event at the 1936 meeting. A public relations committee was created. The main purpose was to invite the press to report on the papers presented and to provide some supervision to prevent misinterpretation. This role would expand in the years to come, and the Academy made some strong efforts in public relations.

In 1937 the meeting was held June 24–26 in Rochester, just before the AOA Convention, in an effort to attract better attendance. This practice continued until 1940 when again the meeting was moved to December. Attendance did improve and total membership also was increasing rather significantly, reaching 157. Business went on as usual, and the various committees had been quite active, though no particular change of direction took place.

An interesting development occurred at the Seventeenth Annual Meeting in Richmond, June 22–24, 1938:[10]

> Chairman Paine also appointed a special committee to be known as the Editorial Committee whose duty it will be to receive, pass judgment, accept or reject papers prepared for delivery before the annual meeting of the Academy at San Francisco next year. Lecturers must prepare sufficient copies of papers so that each member of the committee will receive one. The members of this committee are: Fellows D.G. Hummel, Chairman; Charles Sheard and Robert Beitel.

Prior to that time, it is uncertain how papers were selected for presentation. Apparently the speakers were invited either by the program chairman or by the executive council. In 1933, guidelines were published for preparation of papers for presentation at the annual meeting.[11] They were quite detailed and complete, and certainly adhered to scientific standards. However, there was no explanation of how the selection of papers to be presented was to be made.

Most of the 1930s was a period of slow expansion for the Academy. It grew somewhat stronger in size, but certainly not as rapidly as the members had dreamed of and hoped for. Perhaps a few envisioned it far beyond what it was at that time, but all would be astonished if they could have seen it in 1986. However it was evident some changes needed to be made. Don R. Paine of Topeka, Kansas, became chairman at the 1938 annual meeting. An editorial in the *Western Optical World,* January 1939, summarized, at least in the opinion of the editor, the Academy status at that time, and suggested that Paine might bring about some drastic changes:[12]

> That the American Academy of Optometry has thus far failed to meet the hopes and expectations of its organizers and supporters is conceded, even by its own members.
>
> It is equally true that an active scientific body, working in conjunction and close affiliation with the parent body is desirable, yes, imperative, if optometry is to make efficient headway among kindred organizations in educational and scientific advancement.
>
> Occasionally a new figure looms on the horizon of a venture to bring encouragement and hope to followers. It may occur in any of the various walks of life; in science, in business, in the

professions. In affairs of the Academy, possibly the failures lie in the fact that there is yet to be found a man sufficiently imbued with the need of an active scientific body such as the Academy, and willing to centralize his efforts and devote his time and active endeavors toward the advance of such an organization.

Dr. Paine's article in this issue is encouraging, if for no other reason than it brings to the fore an up-and-coming young man, who has already done some excellent work in his home state of Kansas.

First, Academy membership must be materially increased and its finances augmented by liberal contributions both within and without its membership. In only this way can it be made truly representative in our educational and scientific fields, but this can only be accomplished by a closer relationship with the A.O.A., something in the nature of an educational branch of the national body in fact as well as theory. If this could be brought about, it would be a happy solution for both organizations toward reestablishment of the Scientific Section. The various research agencies, now so inadequately equipped, could be brought into the Academy, there to continue their investigations and research under ideal conditions.

Paine wrote "A Message to Professional Optometry" in the same issue, reviewing the need for professionalism and stressing how the Academy must take stronger leadership.[13] Soon he would take steps to develop a "new Academy" and instigate a number of significant changes.

REFERENCES

1. Ryer EL, Hotaling EE. The American Academy of Optometry. Optom Wkly, May 15, 1930;21(12):420-422, 425.
2. Trans AAO 1930;5:11-12.
3. American Academy of Optometry's meeting. Opt J Rev Optom, Jan 2, 1931;67-(1):24.
4. Annual session of American Academy — officers chosen — program of addresses, papers and discussions. Opt J Rev Optom, Dec 18, 1931;68(25):20.
5. Gregg JR. American Optometric Association: A history. St. Louis. Am Optom Assoc, 1972;354-355.
6. Trans AAO, 1932;7:11-12.
7. Trans AAO, 1933;8:144-145.
8. Trans AAO, 1935;9:154-160.
9. American Academy meets in Chicago. Optom Wkly, Aug 27, 1936;27(28):-787-790.

10. Trans AAO, 1938;12:18.
11. American Academy of Optometry. Am J Optom, July 1933;10(7):267-270.
12. The American Academy of Optometry. W Opt World, Jan 1939;27(1):9.
13. Paine DR, A message to professional optometry. Ibid., 13-14.

CHAPTER 4

The "New" Academy
1940–1949

By 1940 it was evident that the Academy needed an overhaul. Growing pains had taught some lessons and, as is the case periodically in most every organization, drastic change was needed to stimulate new growth. But in addition there was a powerful trend moving in the entire profession that prompted Academy leaders to take some strong steps toward achieving the goals of the Academy, with no major change in the goals themselves.

Chairman Don R. Paine delivered a stirring message at the annual meeting in June of 1939, briefly outlining some actions that should be taken and stating that time had been set aside for discussion. However, the records of the meeting do not show whether or not there was approval of any specific policy changes.[1] But the published transactions, Volume 13, contained a supplement entitled "Fellowship in the American Academy of Optometry," in which Paine discussed the elements of membership requirements, and issues of professionalism and snobbishness. He said:[2]

It is hereby decreed, effective January 1, 1940:

First: That a Board of Regents be established. Its membership to be composed of one Fellow in each state of this Union. It shall be the duty of each member of said Board of Regents to keep in active touch with all Fellows in his respective State, to contact all applicants, personally or through correspondence, and to act as a committee on enforcement of standards. Each Board member shall report annually any infraction of the Fellowship Pledge and shall act in an advisory capacity governing Article IV, Section 1, of the Bylaws.

Second: That as a part of the entrance requirements a Board of Examiners (composed of optometric practitioners) be established before which all candidates for Fellowship must prove their competency as optometric practitioners. The day prior to the annual Congress of the Academy will be reserved for such examinations which will be held at the place chosen for the Congress. It is a time-tested fact within academy circles among all professions that the size, value and pride of membership is commensurate to a large degree upon the distinction and service such a society affords its Fellowships. Such organizations have found through time and experience that the only way to afford such distinction is to admit among its membership only those candidates, who are eligible not only in accordance with certain principles of ethics and professionalism but who can prove before an examining board their qualifications to deserve such membership.

Third: That the privilege be granted all members, to pass an achievement test before the Academy Board of Examiners. The current established members have each complied with the existing entrance requirements extant at the time each was admitted to Fellowship. It therefore, follows that members who are in good standing will not be requested to take an examination of any kind unless they aspire to earn the special certificate of Academy Award provided by the successful passing of the Academy Achievement Test.

That the Academy can ever grow to encourage such higher standards and offer increasingly greater service to its fellowship a graduate course will be offered which is designed to assist candidates to prepare for such examinations as are being instituted. This technical course will be augmented by a bi-monthly magazine to be known as *Archives of the American Academy of Optometry*. A magazine for Fellows of the Academy only, which will contain the papers presented at the annual congress of the Academy.

Paine elaborated further on the revisions and included his arguments for them, along with the great need for professionalism and what it meant.[3] Comment on the Academy's "New Setup" appeared in the *Optometric Weekly:*[4]

Explanation is further made that putting on a white coat and "moving upstairs" is not sufficient qualification for membership. The type of service, influence and education offered by an academy is governed by the caste which makes up its ranks. The Academy believes that if the aims and accomplishments are mediocre, there is a hint that the profession of which it is a part is relatively similar in status.

To those who have advocated a letting down of the bars in entrance requirements such as reduced entrance fees, no entrance examinations, and fewer restrictions on this type and location of practice, explanation is given that this has been tried with other professions with such disappointing results that revisions were made in each case which are similar in principle to those which the Academy is enacting.

The thrust of all of the revisions was to ensure that Academy members were qualified educationally and that they adhered to a standard of ethics. The Board of Regents established a person in each state who was to act as a friend to assist membership applicants, but also to police conformance to standards. The fact that this plan never worked is not at all surprising with forty-eight volunteers expected to do a job that was very difficult.

The matter of the entrance examination would create all sorts of controversy. As might be expected, some thought it unnecessary, unfair, and created a "holier than thou" group, etc. Many firmly believed that the use of the examination and establishment of groups of professional and qualified practitioners would be the salvation of the profession. The files of Academy materials which do exist contain a few letters and articles that illustrate the height of emotion this topic could create. Still, a "manual of instruction" for taking a written and practical examination was prepared and examinations were given at the 1940 meeting in Chicago with over sixty applicants taking the achievement test.

The examination for membership had a sort of "grandfather" clause with requirements depending upon length of practice:

Class 1 — Open to any optometrist who has been in practice more than fifteen years and who is now practicing in an ethical and professional manner, and upon acceptance by the Board of Examiners of ten cases from his own files concisely and completely annotated as outlined in the Manual of Instruction. To obtain "Individual Certification" the candidate may, if he so chooses, take the clinical and written examination.

Class 2 — Open to any optometrist who has been in practice more than five years but less than fifteen, and who is now practicing in an ethical and professional manner and upon acceptance by the Board of Examiners of five case reports from his own files concisely and completely annotated as outlined in the Manual of Instruction, and who has taken and successfully passed a practical examination. It is to be understood that the examination given by the Board is in no way comparable to individual State Board Examinations, but is in the true sense, a screening process by which the Board of Examiners will be able to determine the ability of the candidate to successfully handle the practical problems met in general routine practice.

Class 3 — Open to any optometrist who has been in practice less than five years, and who is now practicing in the prescribed manner and upon acceptance by the Board of Examiners of three case reports from his own files concisely and completely annotated as outlined in the Manual of Instruction, and who has taken and successfully passed both the written and clinical examination as outlined in the manual.

The Academy Examining Board later made a report and laid down a number of requirements for giving the exam such as the number of examining rooms, equipment needed, classroom space and personnel assistance. There was no report of the candidates passing or failing; however, during the year there were several lists of numbers of members, and presumably about thirty were successful in the entrance exam.

The idea of members passing an achievement test was a new one. It provided for those who wished to earn a special certificate by doing so. This sounds like continually proving competency such as became an issue thirty years later. The purpose of this was not clear and it got nowhere. The Academy and its members were too busy with other problems to take time with recertification exams. Still, the idea was expressed, though no doubt ahead of its time.

At the same time it was announced that a new publication would be produced, *The Archives of the American Academy of Optometry.* The year 1940, covering the 1939 annual meeting, was the last year of publication of the *Transactions of the AAO* and in 1941, the *American Journal of Optometry* became the *American Journal of Optometry and Archives of the American Academy of Optometry,* and published papers presented at the annual meetings as well as others. * At the Nineteenth Annual Meeting, plans were developed for the editorial policies of the new publication.[5] There was also an innovation at the Chicago meeting: a ladies program was provided for members' spouses.[6]

This surge of interest in membership requirements and the "get

---

* See the history of the Academy Journal in the Appendix for evidence of this fact.

tough" policy was at least partly a reflection of the growing concern in optometry that recognition by government, education, other professions, and the public was largely because optometry was looked upon as a business. Laws were passed in some states in the 1930s regulating corporate practice and commercialism. Medicine and dentistry were experiencing the same kind of evolution. The AOA in the 1940s took aggressive steps to raise ethical standards and to promote professionalism. Those actions were presumed to be a solution to some of optometry's acute problems. *

In 1942, the AOA launched the Professional Advancement Program.[7] Included in it were public relations, student procurement, and much more, but fundamentally it was designed to change the image of optometry from a business to a profession. The same was true, though perhaps not phrased in the same way, of the Academy's upgrading actions. Indeed, it proposed that every optometrist should become a member. Some of its activities, too, were in public relations.

The Twentieth Annual Meeting was held in Chicago, December 7–9, 1941. It can be imagined what effect the news of the Pearl Harbor attack had, just as the first session was getting started. Still the meeting went on as usual. In spite of great hopes for increasing membership, only six candidates took the entrance exams. Attendance was rather small and apparently not much business was transacted.

A breakfast was held for Academy members during the AOA Congress in Atlantic City in July 1941, with twenty-nine members and ten guests present.[8] The Executive Council also met and transacted some business. This was apparently the first time the Executive Council met at a time other than at the annual meeting. The Executive Committee also met on May 6, 1942, and made, among others, four decisions, two brought on by wartime:

1. To cancel the annual meeting until the wartime conditions were clarified.
2. To eliminate the December 1942 requirement for all applicants to take an entrance examination and to retain the three class requirements for the present.
3. To sponsor the publication of Hering's *Special Sense and Movement of the Eye,* by Williams and Wilkens Company of Baltimore. This

---

* Whether or not raising standards did solve problems for the profession must be judged in terms of the times. Boosting ethical requirements for membership may have produced prestige in the 1940s and 1950s, but in the 1980s it has come to be looked upon with disfavor by some segments of society.

was the first book published by the Academy.

4. To present an award to the practicing optometrist presenting the outstanding paper in 1942, and each year thereafter; also, it invited those interested in preparing papers to contact the chairman of the Program Committee. Then at the next meeting there would be one day devoted to class work demonstration of clinical procedures, and if a Fellow so desired, he could present both a paper and clinical demonstration.

The AOA's Professional Advancement Program was under way by the end of 1942 and Editor Koch editorialized about it:[9]

> The Professional Advancement Program recently adopted by the American Optometric Association contains four major objectives. These are (1) increased membership in the association, (2) enlarged enrollment in optometric undergraduate schools, (3) improved professional and ethical standards for the men now in practice, and (4) the development of a coordinated national public relations program on a statewide basis. The Academy may well be of assistance in the successful carrying out of this project.
>
> The Academy has for years set the standard of optometric practice. This standard has been high, yet each year sees more and more optometrists living up to every and all requirements. Progress is being made in this particular, and the experiences of the Academy of the past are now at the disposal of the A.O.A. in enabling our national association to achieve the present goals set forth in the Professional Advancement Program. The A.O.A. is to be congratulated on this new development, which will add much towards the upbuilding of our profession.

The Professional Advancement Program gave impetus to the AAO to enforce its ethical and educational standards. Ready cooperation was at hand because the director general for the AOA was E. LeRoy Ryer who now for nearly forty years had been striving for the goals of the Academy and had done much to establish the Academy. The AAO created a Council on Professional Advancement to help achievement of the AOA Professional Advancement Program goals.

The war necessitated cancellation of a general meeting in 1943 as well, and the AAO was very quiet for nearly two years. The Executive Council met on August 14, 1943 in Cleveland. The following items were of note:[10]

1. Several local chapters had been established including one in Southern California.

PRESIDENTS OF THE
AMERICAN ACADEMY OF OPTOMETRY

DON R. PAINE
1939–1940

ARTHUR P. WHEELOCK
1941–1944

J. FRED ANDREAE
1945–1946

HAROLD M. FISHER
1947–1948

2. Irvin Borish suggested the establishment of junior academies in optometry schools.
3. Bylaws were changed to permit optometrists in practice twenty years and longer to membership without examination.
4. Twenty-nine new members became fellows. *

"Quiet" is still an apt description of Academy activities until the end of 1944. In the spring, President Wheelock made a trip in some eastern and central states to meet with various officers and members. Arthur Wheelock was a rather interesting person and a bit different than most Academy leaders. He owned a small railroad and apparently became rather wealthy. * * His grandfather had been president of Dartmouth College and he himself was rather colorful, and was remembered with a smile by many.[11]

In July of 1944, the Executive Council met in Cleveland. The main topic of discussion was a plan to establish a junior group at optometric schools. The plan proposed that, according to their scholastic standing, a certain percentage of seniors would be selected for membership and from time to time would hear lectures on ethics and professional practice given by Academy Fellows to stimulate the spirit of professionalism. Examinations for Academy fellowships would be given in some of the schools, with members of the faculty as proctors. Two years after graduation all members of the Junior Academy who had practiced optometry according to Academy standards would be admitted to fellowship.

It was decided to hold the annual meeting at the Stevens Hotel in Chicago, December 10–2, 1944. Announcement of the meeing included a brief item that stresses how times have changed:[12] "Hotel rates are: Single room with bath for one person, $3.25 to $6.00. Double room with bath for two, $4.75 to $9.00. With twin beds, $6.00 to $12.00."

The Twenty-Third Annual Meeting was highly successful. Viewed in terms of the technical papers presented, the attendance, the interest shown by members of the Academy in the problems that were introduced, and by the attitude of the Fellows toward the parts they were to play in the future development of the profession itself, the meeting equalled if not surpassed, any previous meeting. Since the program was

---

* One of them was Neville Schuler, British Guiana. There may have been others from countries outside of USA and Canada before 1943 but his name is the first to show up on published lists.
* * During Wheelock's time all Academy officers had to ride on his railroad if it became possible. It was a line about seven miles long in Central Iowa connecting two major lines and apparently quite profitable. One big advantage was that Wheelock, because of his railroad ownership, could obtain a pass for traveling on other railroads and he took advantage of this and rode railroads long after air travel developed.

held during wartime, there was naturally some apprehension as to the ability of the hotel to serve the group adequately but, despite war restrictions, the sessions were held according to schedule and there were over 100 in attendance. The papers presented were very impressive, and among the participants were Henry Hofstetter, Glenn Fry, Irvin Borish, Matthew Luckiesh and Richard Feinberg. *

The plan to establish a junior organization for optometry students was approved at the Chicago meeting. Chapters of an undergraduate honorary scholastic fraternity were to be formed at the optometric schools. It was decided that such a group of honorary fraternity chapters would be called "Alpha Alpha Omicron," the Hellenized version of the initials of the American Academy of Optometry — a name which had been checked in the National Registry of Greek Letter Fraternities, and was not, at that time, in use.[13] The rules and regulations concerning the Alpha Alpha Omicron were described in an article by Irvin Borish.[14] There is no record available that shows any chapters were organized or what became of this idea. * *

Also adopted was a proposal to incorporate special sections, with contact lenses and orthoptics being suggested. A plan to provide extension education was also proposed and referred for study. A lengthy discussion ensued on the matter of releases to the newspapers of the material contained in Academy papers, because of the tendency of reporters to play up the sensational. A policy was set forth to the effect that all papers given or to be given before the Academy meeting become the property of the organization and that any publicity concerning them must come through the Academy's own press relations committee. Failure to comply with this regulation was to be considered unethical conduct, followed by dismissal from the Academy.

The formation of sections was highly significant. This would lead to the development of "diplomate" status which is a form of certification. The first step was thus taken in 1944. It was the beginning of an interest in and concern about proof of competence in specialty areas. Certainly the Academy took the lead in this activity, which in the late 1970s and in the 1980s would be the subject of widespread attention in optometry.

---

* Individuals other than optometrists such as Matthew Luckiesh had been appearing on the lecture program in recent years and many of these individuals were also AAO members. This indicates the growing recognition of the Academy outside of optometry.
* * About the same time there were efforts to establish student membership in the AOA but this too fell by the wayside. In the 1970s, interest revived and in the 1980s there are student members in both organizations.

The proposal to consider extension education also reflected continuing concern about raising the level of education, and particularly to provide education to keep up with new information after graduation. This concern was not confined to the Academy but was present as well in the AOA and the schools and colleges of optometry. Both the latter provided some continuing education and slowly began to expand their programs. A decade later, the Academy would take a giant step in meeting what was becoming a critical need for postgraduate education.

J. Fred Andreae was elected president in 1944 after having served as secretary for seventeen years. He thus was a major figure in the history of the AAO. In fact he was a major figure in optometry having also been president of the Maryland Optometric Association in 1937 and 1938, president of the American Optometric Association in 1930 and 1931, secretary of the International Board of Examiners in Optometry from 1926 until 1943, and secretary of the Maryland State Board of Optometry from 1917 to 1943. For a seven-year period he was thus secretary of four organizations at the same time. Either there was not very much to do — or he was a very swift worker, or he had lots of help. Taking his place as secretary of the Academy was Carel C. Koch, who was to hold the position for twenty-nine years.

Optometric practices did well during the war years and improvement in financial status no doubt was partly responsible for increase in membership. Interest in local chapters of the Academy was growing. A committee under Ernest A. Hutchinson was promoting their formation and a set of rules and procedures was developed. Five new chapters were formed and seventy-five members joined in 1945. This again raised the issue of belonging to a special group. An editorial by Carel Koch addressed this, and his manner of phrasing it adds some color and feeling of the time:[15]

> Some of these men, however, have doubted the wisdom of their applying or affiliating with a "scientific body." They question the value of such a move to themselves. To be sure, the Academy is a scientific society! And still we believe their doubts to be a mistake. While, certainly some optometrists have managed to flounce through college and then on through the rest of their lives without ever exposing their minds to the maturing influence of exact knowledge, we believe this group to be in the extreme minority and that as a whole most optometrists would benefit by Academy contacts with top-flight fellow practitioners and other experts who are today's leaders in the field of visual care.

It is true, in the field of science there are some intellectual snobs who cherish the notion that theirs is a special language which only initiates can comprehend. The good comradeship of the Academy, however, has long since dispelled any touch of this, if it ever existed, and today one finds the real geniuses of visual science who want nothing better than to communicate their ideas to others and who do not scorn to do so in the simplest and homeliest language possible.

This is one of the real values of the splendid annual sessions of the Academy. The meetings where speaker and audience intermingle and where several days are spent in groups discussing problems of mutual interest are a real treat to all concerned. These annual sessions leave one with memories never to be forgotten and with experiences of great value in every day practice. Despite its scientific background, the Academy is geared to the problems of the optometrist in practice today, and its major job is to serve his needs.

It is probable that Academy officers and members as well would say "Amen" to that today. Certainly the nature of the Academy in 1945 as evidenced by its annual meeting attested to the truth of Koch's statement.

The list of twenty-nine papers presented at the Twenty-Fourth Annual Meeting in Columbus was quite impressive, with an increasing number of speakers with Ph.D. degrees. The sections on orthoptics and contact lenses held sessions, and papers were presented at each. The first honorary life fellowship was conferred on Alpheus Smith, dean of the Ohio State University Graduate School.[16] Membership now totaled 340 with a number of educators and non-optometric scientists on the rolls.

The Academy had been active to a small degree in public relations, and in all cases shown concern about it. During 1945 a speakers bureau was formed with Richard Feinberg as chairman. Rosters were prepared comprised of members qualified and willing to speak, and this was made available to groups looking for speakers.

In the mid 1940s the Academy was awarding small grants for research projects. Among them were grants to Robert E. Bannon, Dartmouth Eye Institute; Glenn Fry, Ohio State University School of Optometry; and Meredith Morgan, University of California School of Optometry. A growing number of researchers was finding the Academy meeting to be an excellent forum for idea exchange and the organization was more and more becoming the "scientific body" its founders had intended. One hundred thirteen people attended the 1945 meeting and an increasing number were educators and scientists.

The record shows no official action establishing sections on pathology and aniseikonia, yet for the 1946 meeting, chairmen were appointed for those sections.[17] The December meeting scheduled for Philadelphia was cancelled at the last minute. The reason was a coal strike that reduced fuel supplies and restricted railroad and hotel services. Instead the meeting was held May 18–21, 1947, at the same location, the Bellevue Stratford Hotel, and with the same program.

In spite of concern about changing the date to May, attendance at the annual meeting was only a few less than at the previous one in Columbus. The program and activities were much the same as the past few years, showing real strength of the Academy. An honorary life fellowship was awarded to James P.C. Southall in absentia. Recognition of such scientists certainly was bringing credit to the Academy and this would be accelerated by additional awards a few years later. Professional ethics was still a major concern and that was the title of the annual banquet presentation by Eugene Freeman.[18] An interesting note in the secretary's report was the suspension of three members for "infraction of the rules relating to optometric practice."

A second meeting in 1947 was held in Chicago, December 13–16. The attendance of over 140 was the best ever, again evidence of the steady growth of the organization. Several more local chapters had been established and things were looking bright for the future. A most momentous action was taken. Chairman John C. Neill reported that the Contact Lens Section had adopted a plan to certify contact lens specialists.[19] Consider that that was just about the time corneal lenses appeared on the scene and the number of optometrists fitting contacts was relatively small. How much furor this decision caused is unknown, but it certainly would have created some a few years later when the question would have been raised as to whether contact lens fitting was actually a specialty. Here are the provisions of the certification process stated at that time:[20]

Purposes of certification and the examining board:
1. To elevate the standards of contact lens practice.
2. To determine the competence of practitioners professing to be specialists in the application of contact lenses.
3. To arrange and conduct examinations to test the qualifications of candidates who appear before the board for certi-

fication as specialists in the application of contact lenses.

4. To grant and issue certificates of qualification as specialists in the application of contact lenses to candidates successful in demonstrating their proficiency.

5. To establish a control panel of diplomates who will act as advisors to candidates for the examinations.

6. To serve the public and the professions by indicating with a designated symbol in the Directory of the American Academy of Optometry that the individual has been certified as a contact lens specialist.

The certificate does not of itself confer on the diplomate any legal qualifications, privileges, or license to practice the application of contact lenses. It is not the purpose or intent in any way to interfere with or to limit the professional activities of any duly licensed optometrist. The chief aim is to elevate the standards of qualification for specialists in the application of contact lenses and to certify as specialists those Fellows of the American Academy of Optometry who appear before the examining board and are successful in meeting the requirements.

All candidates who are presently engaged in contact lens practice and who file application for examination before December, 1948 will be required to submit the records of 20 successful contact lens cases which he has completed, together with evidence of formal instruction or its equivalent in the application of contact lenses. Upon acceptance of these prerequisites by the examining board the candidate will be notified to appear before the board for oral, written and practical examinations which will be given immediately preceding the December, 1948, meeting of the American Academy of Optometry.

Those candidates who file application after Dec. 1948, and who have not completed the prerequisite number of cases will be notified to appear for examinations but the awarding of the certificate will be withheld pending completion of the required number of cases.

Candidates who file application after December, 1948 must:

(a) Submit a statement from an accredited optometric institution showing satisfactory completion of a post-graduate course of instruction in the application of contact lenses.

(b) Submit the records of 20 successful contact lens cases

which have been completed under the supervision of a member of the control panel who has been assigned to the candidate.

(c) Appear before the examining board for a practical, oral and written examination.

All candidates will be examined in the subjects basic to the application of contact lenses. These subjects will include the anatomy, histology and physiology of the anterior segment of the eye and its adnexa, the chemistry of contact lens solutions, the optics of contact lenses and the pathology and therapeutics associated with contact lens practice. The candidate will also be examined in the historical development of contact lenses as well as the modern forms of such lenses, including both moulded and trial case types. The practical examination will be limited to the particular method or methods employed by the candidate in applying contact lenses to the cases reported by him to the examining board; however, he will be expected to be able to discuss intelligently other methods of contact lens application.

In preparing for the examination the candidate will be guided by the syllabus prepared by the examining board. A sample of the form to be used in submitting case records will be furnished the applicant.

The first contact lens certification examination was given at the Twenty-Seventh Annual Meeting in Winston-Salem, North Carolina on December 4–7, 1948. Twenty-one candidates took the examination. Some minor changes were made for future examinations and the next one scheduled for the upcoming annual meeting in Chicago.

Apparently the Winston-Salem meeting had a more "fun" aspect than most. Part of it was because Robert N. Walker, a former president of the Academy, who put in a bid to have the meeting there, came to the Chicago meeting in a chartered Pullman car. That led to four charter Pullmans going to Winston-Salem from various parts of the country. Then there was the matter of southern-barbecued pig that had been promised by Walker.[21]

Following a morning and afternoon session of papers, some of which represented a year's research and preparation by the authors, the membership "cashed in" on a Tar Heel promise made a year ago by Dr. Robert Walker, Winston-Salem, who promised the Academy an old-fashioned southern barbecue pig, with the "deluxe" trimmings, if the city of Winston-Salem were voted as the 1948 convention site. Donning chef apparel, the cigar-chewing Dr. Walker presided over the sizzling porker which was served in the ballroom of the hotel. Optometrists and their wives and guests from all sections of the country voiced their approval of the barbecue which differed from other sectional barbecues only in its southern flavor.

The Academy now was a busy organization with far more activity than the once-a-year meeting that had been nearly its total function for some twenty years. The pages of its journals carried many items of committee functions and meetings of its local chapters. The scientific papers in the journal also were covering a wider range of subjects which were of increasing quality as well.

The Academy had gained considerably in stature in the past decade. In 1949, there were nearly 500 members and 16 local chapters. The number of committees functioning had increased and included committees on admittance, program and papers, nomenclature and standards, screening new instruments and techniques, student counsel, chapters and new chapters, revision on the manual of instruction to applicants, library and museum, research projects, and the editorial council. There were also the sections on contact lenses, pathology, orthoptics and aniseikonia functioning.

Of constant concern was the matter of membership requirements.[*] Like most organizations, the AAO spent a good deal of time amending the bylaws, and in 1949 the method of processing applications was changed again. So were some of the requirements for submitting cases and the nature of the clinical and written examinations. The Academy was beginning to place more and more emphasis not upon ethical requirements as such, but rather upon boosting the professional image in such matters as office appearance and location. But membership requirements must have been generally accepted by optometrists because the Academy was a growing force in optometry and would become even more so in the 1950s.

REFERENCES

1. Trans AAO, 1939;13:15-20.
2. Ibid., 77-82.

[*] A copy of the *Standards of Practice* can be found in the Appendix.

3. Paine D. Revised Academy of Optometry. Opt J Rev Optom, Jan 15, 1940;77 (2):28-30.
4. Academy of Optometry's new setup. Optom Wkly, Feb 1, 1940;30(51):1437.
5. Draws notables Academy meeting. Optom Wkly, Dec 19, 1940;31(45):1272.
6. Andreae JF. American Academy of Optometry. W Optom World, Dec 1940;28 (12):504.
7. The AOA Professional Advancement Program. Opt J Rev Optom, Nov 1, 1942;79(21):22-23.
8. Academy members meet at AOA session. Am J Optom Arch Am Acad Optom, Aug 1941;18(7):329.
9. Koch CC. The Academy and the Professional Advancement Program. Am J Optom Am Acad Optom, Dec 1942;19(12):498-500.
10. Academy annual report. Am J Optom Arch Am Acad Optom, Jan 1944;21(1): 29-32.
11. AAO Living History Videotape of Morgan M, Peters H, and Wick R. Recorded Dec 1984. AAO Archives, ILAMO. St. Louis.
12. Annual meeting of the Academy. Am J Optom Am Acad Optom, Oct 1944;21 (10):429.
13. Academy proposes junior group. Optom Wkly, Dec 21, 1944;35(46):1276.
14. Borish IM. Academy founds national optometric undergraduate scholastic honorary fraternity, Alpha Alpha Omicron. Am J Optom Am Acad Optom, Feb 1945;22(2):92-97.
15. Koch CC. The value of fellowship in the Academy. Am J Optom Am Acad Optom, June 1945;22(6):279-280.
16. American Academy reelects officers. Optom Wk, Dec 20, 1945;36(45):1302.
17. Academy committee appointments. Am J Optom Am Acad Optom, May 1946;23 (5):227.
18. Freeman E. Professional ethics. Am J Optom Am Acad Optom, June 1947;24(6): 284-290.
19. Academy to certify contact lens specialists. Am J Optom Am Acad Optom, Jan 1948;25(1):43.
20. Certification by the Contact Lens Section. Am J Optom Am Acad Optom, Feb 1948;25(2):95-99.
21. Social health and barbecue pit enliven American Academy meeting. Optom Wkly, Dec 23, 1948;39(50):2385.

CHAPTER 5

AAO's Changing Character
1950–1959

The Academy had changed its complexion by 1950. The process had been evolutionary, not revolutionary, so there is no way to state exactly when it happened. However, now the large majority of the individuals presenting papers were educators and/or "scientists," if that is a more appropriate term to describe some of them. Fewer optometrists solely in practice presented papers as compared to earlier years. A great many practitioners were members, but the program now was dominated by educators. In fact there was some concern about the Academy becoming an organization only for scientists and Ph.D.s.*

The list of speakers for the twenty-eighth meeting in Cleveland shows that nineteen of them were educators, seven were scientists from companies or foundations, and six were practicing optometrists.[1]** The

---

* The fact some members were nervous about this was expressed by a past president of the AAO on one of the AAO Living History videotapes. But it is also reflected in some of the articles published at this time.
** The speakers at the Twenty-Eighth Annual Meeting were Glenn Fry, Matthew Alpern, Henry Knoll, George Knox and Vincent Ellerbrock from The Ohio State University, School of Optometry; Howard Bartley, Michigan State College; Paul Boeder, American Optical Company, Southbridge, Massachusetts; Rudolph Ehrenberg, Granite Falls, Minnesota; Richard Feinberg, Pacific University, School of Optometry; Irving P. Filderman, Southern College of Optometry; Eugene Freeman and Z.V. Schoen, Chicago College of Optometry; Henry Hofstetter, Los Angeles College of Optometry; Fred Jobe, Bausch & Lomb Optical Company, Rochester, New York; Sylvester Guth, General Electric Company, Cleveland, Ohio; James H. Grout, Northern Illinois College of Optometry; E.J. Gording, Windber, Pennsylvania; William G. Walton, Frederick Sinn, Onofrey Rybachok, and J. Donald Kratz from Pennsylvania State College of Optometry; Ralph Wick, Rapid City, South Dakota; E. Craig Wilson, Rutland, Vermont; W.O. Vivian, Media, Pennsylvania; Irving I. Vics, Albany, New York; William Smith, Massachusetts College of Optometry; Roy Marks, Lansing Associates, New York City; Alfred Lit, Columbia

annual meetings were becoming "big business," perhaps not as viewed from today's figures but certainly as compared to a few years before. Out of some 500 Academy members, including optometrists, and non-optometric educators and scientists, nearly 200 members and their guests attended the 1950 annual meeting in Chicago, now a four-day session. In order to plan adequately for the meetings, it was decided to select sites two years in advance, and bids were even received for as much as five years ahead. A committee was appointed to "study" convention sites.

Another evidence of a change in its stature is that the Academy was granted the status of an associated society of the American Association for the Advancement of Science.[2] This was done in 1949, and a number of AAO members became AAAS members. It is also obvious from the topics of the papers published in the *Academy Journal* and the qualifications of their authors, as well as those on annual meeting programs, that the Academy was becoming a respected and well-recognized academy of learned men and women. *

The meeting program was also expanding. At the 1952 session there were twenty-nine papers presented and thirty hours of discussion on clinical subjects during the meeting of the various sections. Prominent scientists were often speakers at one of the sessions or at the banquet. For example, Brian O'Brian, a noted physicist, spoke on "Vision and Resolution in the Central Retina" at the Round Table Banquet. There were often visits to an industry relating to visual science during the annual meeting, including General Electric's Nela Park, American Optical Company, and Bausch & Lomb; and a number of times over the years, sessions were held at schools of optometry and tours conducted of clinical facilities. Convention registration lists began to show members and guests from other countries.

Membership in the early 1950s was over 600, though editorials continued to bemoan the fact that there should be many more members, as is so typical of the leaders of voluntary membership organizations, and is still true of AAO today. The number of chapters reached twenty-two and the optometric press frequently published items about their

---

University, School of Optometry; Meredith Morgan, Jr., University of California, School of Optometry; Kenneth N. Ogle and Charles Sheard from Mayo Foundation, Rochester, Minnesota; and Edward Bind, Toronto, Ontario, Canada.
* The membership rosters and programs show very few women up to this time and even for the next several decades. One reason was simply because the numbers in education or clinical practice were very small. In recent years, however, the numbers of women have increased dramatically.

meetings and their programs from California to Washington to Texas to Florida to New York.* Things were booming in optometric academy circles, so to speak.

The number of chapters continued to grow, one or two being added each year in the early 1950s, though others became inactive. There was talk of regionalization, and review of membership applications was begun on a regional basis. A Western Regional Meeting was held at Berkeley, California, on April 10 and 11, 1954. Twenty papers were presented by an impressive array of speakers. In fact, the growth of optometry scientifically is shown by comparison of topics and speakers, including their qualifications, over the years. It would occupy too much space to reproduce detailed comparisons here, but records clearly demonstrate this.

It was a struggle for the Academy to support research, but it was trying, and these efforts were improving its image. The financial reports consistently showed it to be in the black with a small balance on hand. A tight rein on expenditures was the reason rather than a large cash inflow. Dues collection seemed to be a minor problem, though each year a few members were dropped for nonpayment. Still, a few project grants were made in 1949, and the Research Committee summarized them, showing the types of subjects of interest at the time:[3]

Columbia University, Dr. William Feinbloom, *Problems of Strabismus.* $2,000.

Columbia University, Dr. William Feinbloom, *Report of 500 Cases of Subnormal Vision.* $500.

Clark University, Dr. Robert J. Beitel, *Visual Threshold.* $300.

University of Minnesota, Dr. J.I. Kurtz, *Reliability of Near Point Accommodative Tests.* $350.

Columbia University, Dr. William Feinbloom, *Visual Rehabilitation.* $200.

University of Southern California, Dr. Brant Clark, *Binocular Behavior of Eyes — Photographic Study.* $100.

Pennsylvania State College of Optometry, Dr. William J. Tait, *Fusional Convergence Amplitude Study.* $150.

George Washington University, Dr. Lewis H. Kraskin, *Emo-*

---

* It is difficult to determine which chapters were actually officially recognized by the national body. Some were chartered, paid dues for awhile, then continued on their own using the same name. Press reports and even Academy records were never completely accurate, so the actual numbers at any one time may have been more or less. See Appendix for more on history of the chapters.

ional Disorders and Their Effect on Vision. $150.

University of California, Dr. Meredith W. Morgan, Jr., *Studies in Binocular Vision*. $500.

Dartmouth College, Dr. Robert E. Bannon, *Study of Cycloplegic Refraction*. $1,000.

The Ohio State University, Drs. Glenn A. Fry and Henry Knoll. *An Investigation of the Low Levels of Illumination and Freedom of Optical Stimulation upon the Refractive State of the Eye*. Parts I and II. $3,000.

Columbia University, Drs. Frank Lit and Aaron Hyman. *Study of the Pulfrich Phenomena*. $2,000.

Another indication of the change in personality, or image, or complexion of the Academy was the election of Meredith W. Morgan as president in 1953 and 1954. Not that that event alone made a drastic change, but it shows a trend toward more participation by educators and scientists than in the beginning. It is interesting that practitioners were the founders and developers of an organization that was needed even more critically by educators and scientists; also that ultimately it became in large their forum, with clinicians maintaining a significant role and gaining a great benefit but certainly not being dominant in the educational aspects.

With the beginning presidency of Frank Brazelton in 1987, there will have been thirty-two chairmen or presidents of the American Academy of Optometry. Of the first sixteen, only one, Meredith Morgan, was primarily an educator.* Of the last sixteen, ten have been optometric educators. By no means is that intended to put down the practitioners nor imply that they were or are not scientists. To the contrary, to succeed in an area of the scientific world requires great skill, knowledge, and perhaps diplomacy. It is also true that several officers prior to Morgan had some role in education, but it was not their primary occupation. Also, some of the "educators" after Morgan were or had been in practice.**

---

* Morgan's predecessor, Harold Simmerman, was also in optometric education, but he earned his living primarily from practice. Morgan also at the time was in practice part-time with his father, but his activity was primarily in optometric education. He was the first president to hold a Ph.D. degree.

** The balance between practitioners and educators on the Executive Council caused some concern from time to time. But an equal balance could not always be maintained, because some members who were practitioners became educators while on the Council and for various other reasons. This point is discussed again later.

The point is made only to demonstrate the changing character of the AAO. Certainly its presidents were not chosen simply because they were educators or clinicians but because they were extremely capable. Beginning at this time, it was the general plan to maintain a balance of practitioners and educators, though in actuality this was not always adhered to. There were concerns that the "control" or "influence" of one group or the other would get out of balance. Thus, from this time on the president of the Academy was generally expected to go through the chairs, a process that could require as long as twelve years to reach the presidency, with two more as immediate past president. In 1982 the secretary-treasurer position became an office held by each person "going through the chairs." Thus, at present going through the presidency can mean being on the Executive Council for as long as sixteen years.

The sections were also expanded as the organization grew, and the Section on Occupational Vision was established in 1951. This section held its first meeting for presentation of papers in Rochester in December 1952, and a series of seven topics was discussed, including job analysis, third-party care, and illumination. There also was a general discussion of occupational vision.

It was at that time that the American Optometric Association began to press very hard for adherence to a code of ethics as a requirement for membership. In 1950 the AOA Rules of Practice were adopted.[4] The Academy applauded this and at the same time felt some vindication of the stand it had always taken on high-level ethics. The AAO promised to help the AOA improve conformance to the code and found it easier to obtain members because of the general drive in the profession for stricter membership requirements.

There is no way to judge the long-range effects of the Rules of Practice and the Academy's activity in this area. Certainly critical problems developed for the AOA, including a drop in membership in some cases.[5] The issue probably did not negatively affect the AAO. But the fact is interesting that, in a sense, its stand on ethics up to that time in history had been proven correct, and now even the political organization of the profession was aggressively taking the same path to eliminate what were considered ills in the delivery of vision care.

It might be judged that the methods applied to enforce ethics did not work, in fact may have backfired. Thirty years later it might be looked at that way in light of what has happened. Still, what if the AAO and the AOA had not fought for ethics and professionalism and against commercialism? Would the quality of health-care delivery in America have been better or worse? The Academy's role in raising standards at a time when they were greatly needed has been a significant one. Its actions must be evaluated in terms of social, economic, and political pressures of the time in which they were taken. The same is true in the 1980s when the standards are much different.

It is also significant that there apparently was no longer any conflict between the two organizations. Few, if any, articles appeared referring to a "jealous" or "holier-than-thou" attitude. Both AAO and AOA had "grown up" and though there were undoubtedly still some differences, they were handled in a mature fashion, and at the same time, the organizations helped each other to the benefit of both. This new era of harmony is shown by a resolution passed by the AAO Executive Council after meeting in joint session with the AOA Board of Trustees in New York in December 1951:[6]

> *Whereas:* The American Optometric Association, with its affiliated State and local associations constitutes the first line of defense for optometry without which the profession rapidly would suffer irreparable injury if not complete disintegration; now, therefore, be it
>
> *Resolved:* That we as Fellows of the American Academy in the annual meeting assembled hereby go on record as favoring the closest association with the American Optometric Association and its affiliated State and local associations; and, be it further
>
> *Resolved:* That only under very exceptional circumstances should an Academy Fellow actively engaged in practice in the U.S.A. be considered free from obligation of membership in his local, State, and the American Optometric Association.

The changing character of the Academy, namely paper sessions trending toward a forum for reporting research results and theory analysis somewhat remote from the immediate needs of the optometric practitioner, to some degree reduced the value of attending the annual meetings. Clinicians came to get educated and talk about the day-to-day problems they faced in practice. Rapid expansion of knowledge in clinical optometry as well as visual science was leaving behind some who had graduated more than a few years ago. At this period in time there were limited sources of continuing education. Also, contact lenses, low vision, and much in recognition of pathology were relatively new. There was a need for education that the Academy program was not filling.

One of the recommendations adopted by the Executive Council in

December 1950 was that the Academy study plans for short courses in aniseikonia, orthoptics, and contact lenses, in cooperation with the schools in the convention city prior to the annual Academy meetings.[7]

That was the first step taken to institute what was to become an extensive postgraduate education program offered by the Academy prior to its usual annual meeting. By 1986 it had grown to 125 courses, covering 223 lecture hours by 101 speakers, ranging from clinical to legal to research to theoretical subjects. But it took time to get started, and a unique format developed to make it financially sound, yet attractive and affordable to participants.

The matter of postgraduate courses apparently got little attention, because there is no indication of any activity until 1953, when once again the idea was considered by the Executive Council and this time a committee appointed.[8]

The committee was to study and review the proposal of annually presenting five-day clinical and theoretical graduate courses for optometrists immediately prior to or following the annual meetings of the Academy. The courses were expected to cover refraction and examination techniques as well as certain of the more specialized optometric procedures such as contact lens fitting, aniseikonic corrections, and others. Appointed to the committee were V.J. Ellerbrock, chairman, Columbus, Ohio; J. Donald Kratz, Souderton, Pennsylvania; Charles Stewart, Houston, Texas; and Carel C. Koch, Minneapolis, Minnesota.

At the same time, two other actions were taken to improve the educational program. The Executive Council considered the matter of arranging an annual special invitation paper, with suitable honorarium, to be presented before the annual meetings of the Academy in the future. To study and plan for this proposal, the council appointed a committee, with Henry W. Hofstetter, chairman, Bloomington, Indiana; Glenn A. Fry, Columbus, Ohio; Gordon L. Walls, Berkeley, California; and John D. Perry, Winston-Salem, North Carolina, as members.

The Executive Committee also considered the proposal to have a series of five-minute research summaries prepared and presented annually at future meetings by men currently carrying on these research projects in the educational institutions. These reports were to be in the nature of progress reports only. The Papers and Program Committee was requested to review and implement this proposal if the Committee found it to be practical.

This time there was action, and the following year, both the concepts

PRESIDENTS OF THE
AMERICAN ACADEMY OF OPTOMETRY

DANIEL G. HUMMEL
1949–1950

HAROLD SIMMERMAN
1951–1952

PRESIDENTS OF THE
AMERICAN ACADEMY OF OPTOMETRY

MEREDITH W. MORGAN
1953–1954

JOHN D. PERRY
1955–1956

ROBERT W. TUBESING
1957–1958

were formally approved. Here is the way they are described in the record:[9]

> The Executive Council approved a recommendation that the Academy sponsor a "Memorial paper and award" on a bi-annual basis, the first medal and award to be made in December, 1956, at Houston, Texas. This action was taken following the presentation of a committee report on this subject by Dr. Henry Hofstetter, chairman of a committee that had been reviewing the matter for some time.
>
> One of the most important roles of the Academy is furtherance and promotion of education for Optometry. To the present time, this role has been met by the presentation of a wide variety of original papers at the national and sectional meetings, publication of original papers, editorials, book reviews, etc. in this Journal, and sponsorship of research projects through grants-in-aid. The Academy now plans to enlarge its services.
>
> For some time it has been realized that graduate courses sponsored by the Academy would serve a very useful purpose. For this reason, the Academy appointed a committee one year ago to study and review this possibility and report at the annual meeting in 1954. This procedure was followed and the recommendation made that such courses be inaugurated in conjunction with but prior to the next annual meeting. This recommendation was accepted by the Executive Council; steps were then taken so that courses might be realized at the next annual meeting. The courses will be open to all optometrists.
>
> The courses will vary in length from one to twelve clock hours. In order to achieve a wide selection, an attempt will be made to keep the courses as short as possible. For courses exceeding six hours, participation of more than one instructor is recommended. At the present it is felt that all courses probably can be offered in two or three days preceding the regular annual meeting.
>
> Members of the American Academy of Optometry will qualify as instructors and offer one or more courses. By this means, it is hoped that the vast reservoir of knowledge, skills and methods in the Academy will be readily available to all optometrists.
>
> The Executive Council appointed V.J. Ellerbrock, Ph.D.,

The Ohio State University, School of Optometry, Columbus, as chairman of the Committee on Instruction, and D.G. Hummel, O.D., Cleveland, chairman of the Committee on Administration for the coming Academy Postgraduate Courses.

The postgraduate courses were started in Chicago at the annual meeting in the Drake Hotel, December 7–9, 1955. There were forty different courses by forty-one instructors, including two ladies, Lois Bing and Margaret Dowaliby, totaling 104 hours of instructions. * The chairman of the Committee on Postgraduate Education, Vincent J. Ellerbrock, directed the program for ten years. A copy of the first program can be found in the Appendix. * *

It was intended that the courses would not supplant any portion of the regular annual meeting of the Academy. Rather, they were to be supplementary, and an addition to the regular meeting. The regular meeting continued to consist of business sessions, scientific reports, and sectional meetings. The courses were also designed to complement rather than compete with programs of postgraduate education by the various schools and colleges of optometry or with state or national organizations or independent groups promoting postgraduate optometric instruction. The Academy courses were intended to represent a new and different approach — a very wide variety of subjects offered with participation of a large number of instructors.

The postgraduate courses, as described by the Committee on Instruction, were expected to emphasize time-proven principles, data, and techniques, in keeping with precedence, original papers, new data and research, and reports of investigations first presented in the general, open scientific sessions of the annual meeting. Also, in the courses, practical, clinical data and methods especially were to be emphasized. However, principles, concepts, hypotheses, and ideas all were to be included. A large order indeed for a continuing education course, but that was the goal set by the Academy.

A standard fee of two dollars per hour per person was charged for each course. Thus, costs and honorariums to instructors were covered, and the program became self-sustaining. Any optometrist, regardless of whether he was an Academy member or not, was eligible for enrollment

---

* These two ladies were probably the first on any Academy program; at least no others were discovered during research for this book.
* * The format for the continuing education program established by the Academy became a method adopted by many optometric groups. The wide choice of courses offered and payment on a per hour basis was very popular and partly accounted for the rapid growth of the Academy's postgraduate programs.

in the courses. This policy was in keeping with the objective of the Academy always to increase and enrich the background of members of the profession. Any member of the American Academy of Optometry could qualify as an instructor and offer one or more courses. By this means, it was hoped that the reservoir of wisdom, knowledge, skills, and clinical methods of members in the Academy would be readily available to all optometrists.

To repeat the oft repeated phrase that history repeats itself is hardly worth repeating. Yet it is so true. This history has many examples. One that might bring a smile to some readers is the following item from the record of the Executive Council in Chicago, December 1955.[10] Not that this action itself took place again in the same way, but the issue involved, the training of technicians, certainly did. And so did long hours of special sessions and expression of opinions by many Academy members:

> During the week in Chicago, the Executive Council was in special session for thirty-two clock hours. Much of this time was devoted to routine Academy business and questions regarding membership and reviewing qualifications of applicants. One problem before the Council, however, required many hours of conference during which a large number of members presented their views and opinions. This question had to do with the teaching and training of technicians by Academy members. As the result of these deliberations the following statement of policy was drafted and approved:
>
> Training Technicians — Statement of Academy policy. The Executive Council of the American Academy of Optometry has considered the teaching of professional and technical procedures by Academy members to non-professional personnel. The Council recognizes the democratic principle of freedom in the pursuit of truth and knowledge and wants to avoid any interference with this principle as it applies to the members of the Academy. However, the Council also recognizes the principle that the welfare of the public is the primary concern of our profession. It is possible that actions of Academy members cannot be guided simultaneously by both of these principles. As these principles relate to Academy members teaching non-professional personnel, the Council urges members to use every care that such students have sufficient preliminary education and be subject to adequate professional supervision so that

their knowledge of professional procedures does not endanger the welfare of the public.

Another issue in regard to teaching others arose in 1956. The resolution above about teaching technicians was certainly stated delicately: "It is possible that actions of Academy members cannot be guided simultaneously by both of these principles." However, in the case of teaching the fitting of contact lenses, members were given no choice, and it was stated that the resolution had been "cleared through the legal department of the Academy":[11]

> *Whereas,* it is the obligation of Fellows of the American Academy to disseminate knowledge and
>
> *Whereas,* it is also, in the field of education, the obligation of Fellows of the American Academy of Optometry to protect the welfare of the public, and
>
> *Whereas,* in the opinion of the American Academy of Optometry only individuals who have legal responsibility to the public in the field of refractive care, *i.e.,* optometrists and ophthalmologists, should engage in contact lens fitting, therefore be it
>
> *Resolved,* that Fellows of the American Academy of Optometry may disseminate, teach or in any manner convey knowledge of the art and science of contact lens fitting only to licensed optometrists and ophthalmologists and to students taking courses in accepted and accredited institutions of higher learning existing for the purpose of preparation for licensure in the field of refractive eye care.

The Academy had by mid-1950 developed a character of which its members could be justly proud. This was a fundamental reason for its growing success. A *Journal* editorial, "Academy Encourages Freedom of Thought," describes this quite eloquently and provides another insight into its character.[12]

> The Academy is a powerful force for good in optometry for the very reason that there is no dogma, strict sets of tenets, or party line handed down from above. Each Fellow is respected as an individual who, in gaining his Fellowship, has demonstrated his excellent qualifications. Each Fellow is both entitled and expected to have his own opinion; nor is any Fellow or officer of the Academy expected to withhold his opinions merely because of Academy affiliation.

This freedom of thought among academicians is not merely restricted to scientific affairs, but includes concepts of philosophy, professionalism, as well as completely non-optometric aspects of human thought such as politics and religion. The Academy recognizes the value of divergence of thought in all aspects of intellectual activity, and freedom of thought or expression.

Optometry is seemingly at a point in its development where unanimity of thought is far from an actuality. Such unanimity of thought can never be forced and, in fact, is never realized. Were there no disagreement among men with respect both to the scientific and the professional aspects of optometry, it would mean either that independent thinking had been suspended or that the field was so sterile that all could agree. There is unanimity in the Academy on this point at least, and that is that both of these possibilities are not actualities.

Finally, and in the same vein, all Fellows are urged to attend the Annual Meeting in Toronto next month to see how optometric science is advanced through divergent opinions. In our young profession which unfortunately often is characterized by the blind adherence to specific dogma, it is enlightening indeed to see and hear academicians exhibiting scientific scepticism, but also respecting each other's opinion and intellectual integrity. As a result of these annual meetings, optometric science benefits far more from dissent and disagreement than through blind acceptance of questionable material. We challenge any optometrist to attend an annual meeting and not come away feeling prouder of his profession. It just can't be done.

There were other reasons for members to be proud of the Academy. It was doing a variety of things which not only provided a benefit to members but made it attractive as well. Here are some additional items of interest that occurred during this character-changing period:

• For the first time in its thirty-four-year history, the American Academy of Optometry held a meeting outside the boundaries of the United States, and the experiment resulted in one of the most enjoyable annual affairs the august group had yet presented. The annual meeting was staged by an enthusiastic group of Canadians in the Royal York Hotel, Toronto, Canada, December 11 through 14, 1954. The words of one reporter described the event as follows:[13]

The registration of approximately 200 members from forty-two states and seven Canadian provincial optometric societies and two Canadian schools, made this one of the most outstanding meetings ever to be held. E.J. Fisher, dean of the College of Optometry of Ontario, the Canadian hosts, did an outstanding job in extending their hospitality to the American visitors.

Climax of the four-day session was the annual banquet held in the grand ballroom of the Royal York. The Canadians demonstrated their ability to stage what might be an otherwise routine American style affair by putting on some traditional touches, and thereby giving their American guests something to be long remembered. Each guest found a specially printed menu and program for the ceremonies at his plate. Before starting the meal, the entire company tendered a toast to Queen Elizabeth and to the President of the United States and joined in singing the British national anthem and *America.* It seems certain that no banquet committee on this side of the border will ever be able to create the sensation which occurred when, just prior to the main course, the lights were dimmed, a blare of trumpets sounded, and there emerged a procession circling the room depicting a scene of the middle-ages. Preceded by the maitre d'hotel, two white garbed chefs carried aloft a tremendous tray bearing an entire quarter of beef, while directly behind them walked two of England's famous "beefeaters" carrying their maces and two trumpeteers and a drummer, all garbed in appropriate authentic costume. Later in the meal a similar ceremony was performed to announce the arrival of the dessert, in this case a famous British delicacy, plum pudding.

- The presidents of the AOA began to attend the annual meeting and were guest speakers at some time during the meeting, generally at the Round Table Banquet.
- The clinical examination for Academy membership was waived for optometrists who passed the National Board Examination. Local chapters were functioning in Canada and England. There were members in eleven countries outside the United States in 1957.[14]
- Established the Charles F. Prentice Medal in 1958 to be awarded to a scientist for a significant contribution to advancement of knowledge in visual science.
- In 1939 the Academy had begun publishing monographs, which were especially produced reprints on a variety of subjects of interest to

optometrists. By 1959, 239 of them had been published and they had proven to be very popular. All cost less than one dollar and most were under fifty cents. The authors were optometrists and visual scientists.[15]

• *Synopsis of Glaucoma*, by Arthur Shlaifer, the text for the first home study course for optometrists, was published in 1959. Also published in 1957 was the *Sheard Volume*, a collection of written papers of Charles Sheard on a variety of topics in visual science.

But certain problems still persisted and a few new ones would crop up in the 1960s. That was natural as the organization grew and became more complicated. However, it also had acquired a background of experience that would be helpful in handling them.

REFERENCES

1. Academy to meet in Cleveland. Am J Optom Arch Am Acad Optom, Oct 1949; 26(10):455-456.
2. Academy joins A.A.S.A. Am J Optom Arch Am Acad Optom, Sept 1949; 26(9):409.
3. Research projects committee report. Am J Optom Arch Am Acad Optom, Jan 1950;27(1):47-48.
4. Proceedings of 53rd Annual Congress of the AOA, Minneapolis, Minn. June 26-28, 1950; Archives of the AOA, ILAMO, St. Louis: 123-160.
5. Gregg JR. American Optometric Association, A History. St. Louis: Am Optom Assoc, 1972:354-355.
6. American Academy of Optometry meets in New York. J Am Optom Assn, Feb 1952; 23(7):436-437.
7. Simmerman heads American Academy of Optometry. J Am Optom Assn, Feb 1951;22(7):411.
8. Executive Council actions. Am J Optom Arch Am Acad Optom, Jan 1954; 31(1):50.
9. Executive Council actions. Am J Optom Arch Am Acad Optom, Jan 1955; 32(1):51-52.
10. The Executive Council. Am J Optom Arch Am Acad Optom, Jan 1956;33(11):56.
11. Resolution on contact lens practice. Am J Optom Arch Am Acad Optom, Jan 1957;34(1):45.
12. Hirsch MJ. Academy encourages freedom of thought. Am J Optom Arch Am Acad Optom, Nov 1954;31(11):583-587.
13. Enthusiastic Canadians play host to 34th American Academy meet. Optom Wkly, Jan 6, 1955;46(1):30-31.
14. The ancillary groups in optometry, Part 1: The American Academy of Optometry. J Am Optom Assn, Oct 1958;30(3):207-208.
15. Academy monographs. Am J Optom Arch Am Acad Optom, Mar 1959; 36(3):156-165.

CHAPTER 6

An Era of
Expanding Prestige and Activity
1960–1969

The 1960s started with the Thirty-Ninth Annual Meeting held in San Francisco, December 11–13, 1960. Membership had reached nearly 1,000 and did pass that mark during the following year. The postgraduate courses enrolled 275 optometrists in seventy-five courses. Lawrence Fitch, who was concluding his second year as president, referred to an interesting point about AOA and AAO relationships:[1]

> During the year, your officers have received criticism of the Academy's policy of requiring that United States optometrists who are applicants for Fellowship in the Academy be members of the American Optometric Association at the time of admission to the Academy. This policy has been in effect for many years and your officers and members of the Executive Council consider it to be just as sound a policy today as it was at the time of inauguration. Although the American Academy of Optometry is organizationally entirely independent of the American Optometric Association with its own distinct objectives, the Academy is complementary and supplementary to the American Optometric Association. All optometrists of the United States, including those who are Academy Fellows, have a moral obligation to belong to the American Optometric Association. It is not practical for the Academy to police its Fellows to see if they maintain membership in the American Optometric Association. However, we know that with very few exceptions, Academy Fellows who are in practice here do retain their membership in the American Optometric Association. This is as it should be. The optometrist who aspires to Fellowship in the Academy should realize that if he is not satisfied with some

aspect of the American Optometric Association, or one of its affiliated state associations, it is his moral responsibility to work for improvement through his membership. He can accomplish nothing through non-membership.

The record of Academy Fellows in their support of the American Optometric Association and participation in its activities speaks for itself. Certainly, Academy Fellows are by far more staunch members of the American Optometric Association than are the optometrists of any cross-section of our practitioners. This fact is very important to our profession in these troubled times of inadequate enrollments in our optometric colleges and unsatisfactory interprofessional relations. Our major mechanism of defense against the unfair and unwarranted attack of misguided politicians of a sister profession is a strong, healthy parent professional organization.

The fact that the AOA president was making a speech at the Round Table Banquet each year also demonstrated that the two organizations were working in harmony. Members of the Academy in the twenties and thirties would probably never have imagined that AOA membership would be required, they possibly would have opposed it. Academy presidents were attending AOA Congresses now as official AAO representatives. Also in the 1960s, there were meetings attended by representatives of AOA, the Association of Schools and Colleges of Optometry, the Optometric Extension Program, the International Board of Examiners, and others. The Academy was generally also invited, and its president, from time to time, served on AOA committees or task forces. The need for and value of each organization was now generally agreed upon.

Thus it seems that the Academy and the AOA each had found its niche in the affairs of optometry. Perhaps that could have been done under some form such as a Scientific Section of the AOA as had once existed, or some other type of organization never even proposed. It is a moot point as to whether the outcome was the best possible solution; however, in the 1960s there were two organizations, and they were functioning effectively in their own spheres. That most likely would satisfy all of the earlier leaders in both organizations who had concerns about what the Academy should do or what the AOA should do, or whether they should merge into one organization, as had once been proposed in the 1950s.[2]

The sections of the Academy by now had grown to assume a very important role. The sections were unique in that they were primarily informal discussion groups devoted to special interests. Papers were presented, but these papers were not necessarily the formal reports of extensive research usually presented to the Academy general sessions. All Fellows interested in the subject matter were invited to participate either in the discussions or in presenting a paper. Seldom were the papers or discussions reported in the journal published by the Academy, so to benefit from these meetings it was necessary to attend in person. Thus they were more clinical in nature, yet not a "course" or an "educational session" as were the postgraduate courses. Discussion was a significant part, not criticism of scientific methodology as such, but questions and comments.

The sections had grown up by 1961 and are described here in some detail to provide a sense of their purpose, scope and function at this point in history:[3]

The Section on Contact Lenses and Subnormal Vision Aids. Robert Graham, Chairman, Pasadena, California.

In recent years the upsurge of interest in contact lenses has been reflected in the activities of this Section. A large and lively group of fellows have regularly attended these discussion sessions. The Section has been called upon to arrange a two-hour symposium on contact lenses for the general session. The Section carries on a certification program and regularly examines and certifies as contact lens specialists those candidates who qualify.

The programs for the coming meeting will be shaped around the following subjects: (a) the accurate determination of corneal topography; (b) bifocal contact lenses; (c) toric, bitoric and perforated contact lenses; (d) current advances in subnormal vision aids; (e) the latest significant developments in the field of contact lenses. Interested Fellows are invited to participate.

The Section on Aniseikonia and Refractive Problems. William P. Schumann, Chairman, Vineland, New Jersey.

Aniseikonia is perhaps the specialty in the field of optometry which demands the greatest exactness in refraction, competence in solving fusional and binocular problems. One of the functions of the Section is to make all Fellows more familiar with aniseikonia and its problems. Case studies and special applications of eikonometry are of special concern. A current problem in this field is the resulting aniseikonia in monocular aphakia corrected by a contact lens.

All optometrists are concerned with the techniques of measurement and interpretation of refractive problems. This Section is interested in discussing and evaluating both new techniques and new instrumentation, as well as theoretical consideration. It is felt that the sessions on refractive problems are of intense practical importance to every Fellow. These sessions serve, too, as a clearing house for possible answers to grief cases, where the combined thought of the group may suggest solutions overlooked by an individual practitioner.

The Section on Binocular Vision and Perception. * Max Schapero, Chairman, Los Angeles, California.

This Section is concerned with the sensory, motor, and perceptual aspects of vision, whether it be monocular or binocular. Six sub-committees have been created to specifically work on major areas of concern. They are: (1) Orthoptics and Visual Training; (2) Reading; (3) Pleoptics; (4) Ocular Motility; (5) Practice Management; (6) Optical Aids for Binocular Vision.

The aims and goals of this Section are to promote interest and understanding in the fields covered, to analyze and discuss recent developments, to promote and present research work, to encourage the writing and publication of papers, and to assist the profession to promote this field. During the Section meeting papers are presented covering all of the topics within the realm of concern, discussions and forums are held, and plans are made to implement the aims of the Section.

Ideas and recommendations that will make the work more effective are always welcome. The Section is especially interested in promoting lively discussions on the topics under consideration.

---

* Members of the Section on Binocular Vision remember with some consternation that one of the individuals very much interested in orthoptics was Lord Charnwood, an optometrist and Academy member from England. He came to the sessions wearing a monocle! Binocular vision? In reality he did wear regular spectacles and used the monocle to attract attention. He came from a famous British family and his father wrote a biography of Abraham Lincoln. In Academy circles he was thought of as a "character," though in a very pleasant sense.

The Section on Pathology. Arthur Shlaifer, Chairman, Philadelphia, Pennsylvania.

One of the functions of the Section on Pathology is to facilitate optometric detection of pathology, either ocular or systemic, which may be encountered. This Section encourages papers at its meetings which bring to the attention of the participants the newest developments in ophthalmology, with respect to both theory and instrumentation.

For example, the most recent contributions to our knowledge of glaucoma, its detection and control, are periodically reviewed.

This Section encourages the presentation of any unusual case report which involves pathology. In addition, it has presented and is continuing to present papers on the photography of ocular pathology. It has in its possession selected films pertaining to ocular pathology which it will lend to interested optometrists.

Although many formal papers are presented, the Section encourages informal discussion by participants in the Section meetings. Thus, it is the intention of the Section to have a degree of active participation by every optometrist attending the meetings.

The Section on Public Health and Occupational Optometry. Galen Kinter, Chairman, Linden, Washington.

Public health optometry is the scientific diagnosis and treatment of the vision needs and status of communities as entities; and includes information necessary for group vision care programs, operation of clinics, industrial and school vision programs, and studies of the visual environment. The general area of concern of this Section is with those aspects of optometry not directly concerned with private clinical practice, but with the vision characteristics and needs of groups.

The activities and concerns of this Section are divided into nine sub-committees; (1) Industrial and/or occupational vision and vision screening, (2) Vision problems of school children and vision screening, (3) Vision problems of transport operations and vision screening, (4) Optometry in group practice, clinics and hospitals, (5) Prepaid vision care programs, (6) Optometry's relations with public health programs, (7) Optometry's participation in civil defense, (8) Optometric participation in veterans and government health programs, (9) Visual environment. It should be obvious that the Academy is interested in the scientific and methodological phases of these problems and not in the political aspects.

The annual meetings continued to grow in attendance, both the postgraduate courses and meeting itself, the total event now requiring seven days. At Chicago's Drake Hotel,* December 6–12, 1961, eighty-one courses were offered and hailed as a gigantic success by the many optometrists who traveled thousands of miles to attend. They were conducted in eight classrooms, and from three to eight classes were held each hour throughout the day and evening. Regarded as a most stimulating course by those attending was the course on the slit-lamp techniques in contact lens work.** As a matter of fact, it was so popular that it was presented on three separate occasions. There were forty-one papers presented and the five sections also conducted extensive programs.

As the Academy grew in size and complexity, more problems arose and there was more business to transact. The Executive Council always met at length to handle business affairs, now requiring so much time the Council members could not always attend the educational sessions they wished. The housekeeping functions had to be dealt with efficiently and regularly. These were not reported in any detail in the published transactions of the Academy, nor in fact were but a few of the business activities or official actions of the Council. The published reports, generally short and with little explanation of reasons for action, were often in the form of a summary of what took place, written by the secretary, or in some cases by one of his assistants. There were apparently no official minutes kept, at least up until the 1960s. But that changed as the business affairs increased and responsibility became greater.***

---

* The Academy generally held its annual meeting at the finest hotels. This created a feeling of prestige, both in the minds of members and the public as well. The Drake was an elegant hotel in its day in Chicago, and the Academy met there many times, through most of the 1950s and the 1960s every other year.

** This shows the changing practice patterns and responsibility of optometrists. Slit-lamp instruments were rarely used before this time.

*** Beginning in the 1960s, minutes of Executive Council were produced in mimeographed form, though they varied and were not always complete. These are preserved in the Academy's Washington office and some individuals possess a few of them. Some also are in the Academy Archives at ILAMO. They have been used as background material for preparation of this history; however, the collection is not complete and other sources have been used as well.

Perhaps the fact the Academy was not a political body accounts for the fact the business affairs were de-emphasized. It may also be true that it was intended that there not be an extensive permanent record of "official" actions. Another factor may be that it was because Carel C. Koch was the secretary for so many years. He was extremely dedicated and effective and every president was exceedingly lavish in praise for his great work, and it was repeated so often by all of them that it was obviously more than the customary "thanks" to the secretary for good work. One president said that Koch was a very dominant figure; he recorded what he wanted to and acted on what he was in favor of, and other items were somehow forgotten. * That comment is not intended to discredit Koch. To the contrary, he was highly revered and the Academy owes more to him than any other person.

But business items had to be dealt with, some minor, others perplexing and controversial, and certainly the number expanding each year. Koch helped presidents maneuver through it all, but the trail is not clear in existing documents up to this time. Here is a list of some of the matters considered and disposed of at the December 5–11, 1962, meeting of the Executive Council, presided over by President Ralph E. Wick, in Miami Beach:[4]

> Reports of officers and committee chairmen for the year 1962.
>
> Reports of officers to be read at the business session of the Academy at Miami Beach.
>
> Communications and personal reports from members of the British Chapter regarding changes brought about by the proposed common market program in Europe and a proposal for a change in the name of the Chapter, to the European Chapter of the Academy.

---

* One president called Koch a "benevolent dictator." Talking to many academy officers and listening to seven hours of videotapes of living Academy history recorded by some dozen Academy leaders leaves no doubt that during Koch's years as secretary it was not a truly democratic organization. The fact that for many years there are no extant minutes and for others they are far from complete is evidence of this. Few men ever became members of the Executive Council without Koch's blessing. All agreed that his judgments were generally sound and that the welfare of the Academy was always his major concern. He was a unique and capable individual and the Academy was indeed fortunate to have his dedicated service for so many years. Koch's contributions to the profession as a whole were recognized in 1972 when he was honored by receiving the American Optometric Association's prestigious Apollo Award.

The matter of more effective handling of applicants who were graduate students working for advanced degrees.

The question of whether to certify aniseikonic clinicians. It was proposed that the Section first make out a complete list of optometrists who fall into this category.

The report of the Committee on Admittance. A detailed review of the applicants qualifying for Fellowship at Miami Beach and the approval of this committee's report. A vote of approval on these applicants. There were 41.

Met with a delegation of members interested in reading problems and the part optometry should play in this matter. It was agreed that those phases of reading problems which fall within the sphere of optometry should be considered by the Section on Binocular Vision and Perception.

Appointed and reviewed the work of the Auditing Committee and the Time and Place Committee.

Appointed a nominating committee.

Considered and rejected a resolution by the New Jersey Chapter to the effect that all Academy members must retain membership in their State Optometric Association to retain their Fellowship in the Academy.

Considered the evidence presented in five cases where the practice standards of Fellows were questioned. Each of these cases was resolved or put on the agenda for further investigations.

Considered and rejected, at the section chairmen's request, certain proposed changes in programming section meetings at future Academy conventions.

Requested each section chairman to appoint, with the approval of the Section, a vice-chairman who will back-stop the chairman and be a candidate at a later date.

Acted on reinstatement of two members.

Considered certain modifications of the Academy Constitution and Bylaws and reappointed an Ad Hoc Committee to consider these and report back at the next meeting.

Considered the report of a Fellow that another had pirated his ideas and had attempted to patent and market them. Secretary instructed to investigate.

Appointed a new editorial council and reviewed the duties of members.

Received and reviewed the report of the registration desk at the Miami Beach convention.

Reviewed the work of the Contact Lens Section examining committee, and after study ruled that in the future the Section make no changes in the manner of certifying Diplomates without first clearing the matter before the Executive Council.

Received the activities of the Committee on Admittance. The Council praised the work of the Committee, approved certain changes on the membership of regional committees and approved the new members of the committees.

That gives a rough idea of the ranges of items with which the Executive Council had to deal — and the need for detailed and documented records. There were few business meetings between the annual meetings, but Secretary Koch handled the myriad of details involved in the business affairs from day to day. He had a small staff in his office in Minneapolis, but he was responsible for publication of the *Academy Journal,* as well as functioning in what amounted to an executive secretary or administrator capacity, though he never carried either title. The Academy was functioning quite well but the time had come for more official record-keeping and more assistance for the Secretary. In 1967 John Schoen was appointed as an assistant secretary, a position he held until he became secretary in December 1973. In 1968 Leo Mayer was added as a deputy secretary, a position he also filled under John Schoen until 1976.

In addition to the meeting in Miami Beach, there was a post–Academy meeting tour to Bogata, Columbia.[5] The purpose was to participate in an international professional forum sponsored by the Columbian Optometric Association. On the three-day program of educational presentations were a number of Academy members and optometrists from Columbia. One paper of particular interest was by an M.D., Jose I. Barraquer, dealing with the present state of refractive surgery, including the premier showing of a film describing the surgical technique.

There were two other items of interest at the Miami Beach meeting, one clinical and one social. One of the special presentations that attracted a large audience was the symposium on tonometry presented by Elwin Marg of Berkeley, California; W.L. Firendi, San Jose, California; Allen A. Isen, Buffalo, New York; and Paul F. Shulman, Chicago, Illinois. Following the presentation of these papers, the audience supplied the panel with more than fifty written questions to be discussed by

PRESIDENTS OF THE
AMERICAN ACADEMY OF OPTOMETRY

LAWRENCE FITCH
1959–1960

RALPH C. WICK
1961–1962

PRESIDENTS OF THE
AMERICAN ACADEMY OF OPTOMETRY

DONALD SPRINGER
1963–1964

J. DONALD KRATZ
1965–1966

MONROE J. HIRSCH
1967–1968

the panelists. This was evidence of the growing interest in glaucoma, just at the threshold of widespread usage of non-contact tonometry. The Academy was in the forefront of this activity.

The other event of interest was a program for wives of Academy members. This was planned by the local arrangements committee members and their wives. A few programs for ladies had been offered previously, but since Miami Beach, the ladies program has grown and become a regular event at the annual meeting.

A highlight of 1963 was the presentation of the first Prentice Medal* to W.A.H. Rushton at the annual meeting in Chicago, December 4–10, at the Academy's usual Chicago home, the Drake Hotel. Rushton's work was briefly summarized as follows:[6]

> Dr. Rushton has revolutionized the knowledge of visual sensation at the retinal level by perfecting a technique for measuring rhodopsin concentration in the living human retina. On the basis of such measurements he was able to delineate the contribution of photochemical factors in the visual process. This had been attempted earlier, on much less convincing evidence, by the late Selig Hecht of Columbia University.
>
> More recently Dr. Rushton's attention has been directed to cone vision. He has now demonstrated that the normal human retina contains at least two cone pigments, which he has called "chlorolabe" and "erythrolabe." Chlorolabe is a green-sensitive photopigment and its absence causes the color vision anomaly known as deuteranopia, while the absence of erythrolabe, a red-sensitive pigment, is the cause of protanopia.

Rushton, as a world renowned scientist and dealing with a very sophisticated topic, gave the Academy a great deal of prestige by appearing on its program and receiving its highest award. This could not have happened until the Academy itself had gained appropriate stature to be recognized by famous scientists. The Academy, because of both its programs and its publications, was now attracting the attention of many top level investigators in vision research. At this same time, an idea was born to let the public know more about vision through a Science Information Program.

The Executive Council in December 1963 at the annual meeting in

---

* Charles Prentice was a pioneer optometrist and a renowned vision scientist. He was instrumental in founding the AOA and passage of laws regulating optometry.

Chicago approved the Science Information Program concept of requesting Fellows for a voluntary assessment to cover program costs. A committee was appointed with William Feinbloom as chairman. The plan was to review papers published in the *Journal*, to prepare educational information based on them for the public press, and to do so once a month. The project was begun in July 1964.[7] The first news article was about the use of daytime automobile lights reducing accidents, and this received considerable news coverage. But from then on, results were less than hoped for.

During the next few months, topics included eye protection to reduce eye injuries, solution to visual problems of the Cuna Indians, and vision training as a remedy for reading problems. Like all committees, or even individuals, who send what they consider items of interest on scientific subjects to the public press, the AAO committee was disappointed with results because more did not appear. The fault was likely that expectations were set too high, not that the program method itself was poorly designed or that there was great lack of understanding of the importance of the subject by editors. The committee learned some significant points, certain of which reflected upon the work the Academy had done and on what it should do in the future. They were summarized:

- Rather than slavishly adhere to a one-a-month timetable, it is better to issue releases only when there is material that is reasonably certain to find response. To do otherwise would mean risk of the standards set and this, in turn, would impair acceptability to the press.
- There was reasonable receptivity. There was no overt rejection of the material because of disparagement of its optometric source.
- Optometry as seen through the eyes of the writers and editors might be expected because of their historic contacts with other areas of science, to regard optometry as a para-medical field and, therefore, to disregard or to dismiss it. Such was not found to be the case.
- There was a surprising degree of ignorance concerning the nomenclature and functions, education and degree of optometrists, ophthalmologists and opticians.
- The press reacted with some surprise to their new knowledge that optometrists systematically devote time and effort to research in disorders of the eyes, to developing new instrumentation, to refining clinical procedures, to measuring

and evaluating treatments, and to investigating matters of vision which pertain to public, as contrasted to individual, problems.

The committee proposed a series of steps that should be taken to inform the press, science writers, and a variety of communications media about optometry and visual science. There was an appeal for support of the voluntary contributions program to keep the project going. Success in 1965 was even greater and a large number of magazines and newspapers published material based upon information supplied to them by the Science Information Committee. A montage of newspaper clippings illustrating the wide coverage that had been achieved was shown to the members. The services of the Barnett Bildersee public relations firm had been contracted for and much of the detail work was being done by its staff. The committee provided supervision and supplied the information suitable for release to the public, religiously avoiding political or controversial issues.

During 1965 the Science Information Program was expanded to include radio and TV sources. A symposium was held in New York City in November with the press invited. The results, it was reported, were very good.[8] At the annual meeting in Denver, a press luncheon was held, with the topic being "Optometric Educational Requirements in the Next Ten Years." This made TV station news in Denver, and the committee, along with the Academy members, was pleased with the growing success. The contract with the Bildersee Company was renewed and plans expanded for the following year. It was proposed that the Academy offer yearly prizes for the best articles in the public press in several categories and programs on radio and TV. This never came to be. However, the AOA about this time began to support a public information program that was similar in nature, including awarding prizes for the best articles. In fact, the activity of the Academy in public relations, or public education as the case may be, raised the question as to whether AOA or AAO should function in this area, and which might have the most resources to do so most effectively. Should both be involved or would a single information source produce the greatest results was the question both organizations considered. This point was discussed by the AAO Executive Council at its 1969 meeting.[9] After conferences with the AOA, the Academy stopped its Science Information Program and the activities in public relations and information. Later the AOA took over most of this function.

An issue that scientific bodies often must deal with, as do indeed political bodies in a certain sense, is whether or not the body "believes," "supports," "promotes," or whatever is the appropriate term, a certain theory or method of practice. The Academy has faced this sort of thing numerous times over the years and no doubt will continue to do so for ages to come. An editorial addressed this question in the *Optometric World* in December 1964. Here are a few excerpts which describe the nature of the Academy, perhaps just as was intended by its founders and quite likely as it would be accurately typified today:[10]

> Despite the 40-year history of following no one optometric philsophy, one does hear from time to time the claim made by an uninformed person that the Academy does or does not believe certain things. Thus, twenty-five years ago it was stated that "the Academy does not believe in orthoptics." (This, in spite of its section on orthoptics.) More recently, the Academy has been accused of being opposed to the "functional approach." The myth changes from time to time in content, but the structure of it remains the same.
>
> The basis for the myth that the Academy has a specific approach to optometric practice stems from those who propose approaches or techniques and are either unwilling or unable to present them in such a fashion to convince their peers. Those who are willing to speculate rather than to prove tend to be annoyed with those who demand evidence.
>
> When asked "Why don't you believe in technique X?" the Academy Fellow is likely to answer, "Why should I believe it?" In short, the burden of proof rests with the proponent. Scientific facts (and clinical ones) are not because someone says they are so. They are useful only when they have been demonstrated to be true and valid.
>
> But even here, when a fact has been demonstrated as valid, the Academy per se takes no action. The members, as individuals, accept or reject evidence. The Academy is a forum and is without dogma. The Academy's function is to contribute the environment in which scientific inquiry may flourish and to help disseminate valid information. Its function is not to approve or disapprove specific techniques or methods.

By no means is it likely that this statement put such an issue totally at rest. No doubt since then, and even today, the Academy, as are most scientific bodies, is thought by some to be a proponent of certain concepts. But the above statement certainly describes the proper attitude of the Academy and the one its members should maintain. Throughout its history it has, as much as possible, held to a "let's see the evidence first" stance.

The Academy functions continued as usual in the latter half of the 1960s, but the organization was beginning to face additional issues as well. The annual meetings were getting larger and there were more continuing education courses and more papers presented, and thus the Executive Council was gaining courage to expand its activity with a membership exceeding 1,500. Two significant actions were taken to enhance the organization's role and service as a scientific body.

At the annual meeting in Columbus in 1964, a bibliographic consultant service had been offered for the first time. Grace Weiner, librarian at the Los Angeles College of Optometry, had a display of books, a book reference list, and provided service as a reference consultant.* In December 1965, the Executive Council approved support of a project to prepare and publish a cumulative index of the first forty-four years of the *Academy Journal* in its various forms. It had been started the year before by a grant from the Auxiliary to the AOA, with Weiner as the bibliographer. This was completed in 1968 and became a valuable source of reference in the field of visual science.[11] Years 1968–1983 were completed by Allison Howard and published in 1985.[12]

Also approved in Columbus and funded was a study to establsh a Visual Science Information Retrieval Center with the two primary functions being regular issuance of an index of available materials in visual science and bibliographic service in connection with libraries and appropriate institutions.[13] This became a reality and was established at the University of California, Berkeley, with the aid of grants from the U.S. Public Health Service. Though not actually an Academy function, the organization was still instrumental in the establishment of the service so useful to scientists and researchers.

Here are some other events and actions that highlighted the last of the 1960s, certainly a successful decade for the AAO:

- In 1967 the extension of the Academy certification program to the field of orthoptics and vision training was established, to be supervised by the Section on Binocular Vision and Perception. The name of the Section on Refractive Problems and Anisekonia was changed to Section on Refractive Problems.

- The postgraduate courses became the Ellerbrock Postgraduate

---

* Grace Weiner provided services to the Academy for many years as bibliographic editor of the *Journal*, 1958–1968, and associate editor, 1968–1975.

Courses. Vincent Ellerbrock had died suddenly, just two days before the beginning of the 1965 program. He was the first chairman of the committee and still was at the time of his death.[14] He had thus directed the highly successful program for ten years and in his honor the name was changed.

▪ Perhaps not in the category of major events but certainly one that Academy members have enjoyed and looked forward to as part of the social activity of the annual meeting was the annual Hofbrau. It gave optometric musicians a chance each year to play before an audience. Academy members enjoyed what they heard as evidenced by the fact that many danced to the music with gusto. The first one was described as follows:[15]

> The meeting [1967] closed on Tuesday night with the First Annual Hofbrau. The dinner was a tremendous success. This was the first of its kind and will probably become an annual event. Following the buffet, the floor was cleared of tables and a five-piece orchestra supplied by Dr. and Mrs. George N. Jessen appeared and took their places. This orchestra served to furnish the musical background for the optometrists who then performed on their instruments for the 250 persons present. The leaders in this portion of the program were Dr. Otto J. Bebber of Lakewood, Colorado, Dr. James N. McBride of Billings, Montana, and Dr. Charles R. Stewart of Waco, Texas, followed by a number of other optometric performers who played, sang and danced to the vast enjoyment of all. We have long known that the Academy is full of extroverts and now we are finding that it also harbors many good musicians. What will the future bring? This dinner meeting was a huge success and we are indebted to the Jessens for their help in making it so.

▪ A new section on Communications and Information was established, also in 1967. It was to deal with information retrieval, computers, writing, audiovisual techniques, clinical research and more. This move was warmly applauded by an editorial in the *Optometric Weekly* which stated that optometrists badly needed to improve the ability to communicate.[16]

▪ Though only a few years before, officers emphasized that the Academy meetings were primarily educational and a forum for scientists, and only a brief time was spent on business, there was a lot of business to deal with. What the officers said about the time on business spent by the members was true, but not for the Executive Council. At the 1968 annual meeting in Beverly Hills, California, the council met during the entire six days.[17] Besides the Executive Committee and six sections, there were the following committees: Admittance, chapters and charters, convention headquarters, editorial council, Ellerbrock postgraduate courses, monograph series, optometric education for service personnel, papers and programs, Prentice medal, science information program, student counsel, synopsis books, and time and place, with over 100 members serving on some committee or council.

• The burden on the secretary's office had escalated beyond the capabilities of one person. An assistant to Carel Koch, John Schoen, was appointed and additional office assistance provided. In 1968, Monroe J. Hirsch became editor of the Academy's *Journal* and Koch was thus relieved of some work, though he continued on as publisher. Koch was presented a plaque for his twenty-five years of service as secretary-treasurer.[18]

The Forty-Eighth Annual Meeting was held in Philadelphia, December 11–16, 1969, to help the Pennsylvania College of Optometry celebrate its fiftieth anniversary. President E.J. Fisher's address stressed the historical significance of this fact and that the city was also the "Cradle of American Liberty" and had a very important role to play in the early history of optometry in America.[19] Fisher spoke about "the Academy in the 1970s." He pointed out that some changes in administrative structure would have to be made because of the burgeoning size of the membership and activities. But also the number of papers presented at the meeting and to be published was creating pressure on time and space. Future executive councils would be challenged to find solutions.

What was the Academy really like in the latter 1960's? The October 1966 issue of the *Journal of the American Optometric Association* dealt almost exclusively with the Academy. The editorial by Milton J. Eger, "The American Academy of Optometry: Vehicle for Education and Ethics," was a very strong commendation of the Academy and its goals of improving education and ethics. The goals were delineated by AAO President J. Donald Kratz. Each of the sections was described and the present status outlined. The postgraduate courses for 1966 were announced and Academy membership qualifications explained, pointing out the AOA membership was required.[20]

In June 1969, the *Journal of the AOA* carried an article about the Academy which was an interview with past president Monroe Hirsch, secretary Carel Koch, and president E.J. Fisher. The question-and-answer format provided an effective method to describe the AAO as it was at that time, in principle little, if any, different than it is in the 1980s, except for one significant change in requirements for membership. Here are a few excerpts of the responses made then:[21]

EDITOR: Gentlemen, let's see if we can't wrap up this interview with one final statement that would be of value to the readers of the *Journal of the AOA* in understanding the function of the Academy.

KOCH: To start it off, let me state that the function of the Academy is merely to interest optometrists, all of them, in doing a better job of practicing optometry. Essentially, that's all we are here for. You might say that's the AOA's job, too. In that sense we duplicate the efforts of the AOA but we approach the problem from a slightly different angle. We are not interested in many of the essential facets of the AOA and what they are doing. We stick, more or less, to the philosophy of bettering your understanding of what you do for your patient. And essentially, we have no other aspect of organizational procedure.

HIRSCH: I think that optometrists should understand that the Academy is anything but an ivory tower organization. The Academy is down to earth and very practical. Optometrists say "give me something practical, practical, practical." I think the Academy is more practical than it is given credit for being. Clinicians and researchers depend on each other and it's this integration that is the Academy's job. By bringing researchers and clinicians together, we are helping the researcher understand what problems need to be solved and helping the clinician to do a better job with his patients.

We have instituted in the *Journal* a new section on Techniques, Instruments and Cases. We are trying to stress clinical application of research because we recognize that research for the sake of research has no value. Unless advances of mankind can ultimately be used for the betterment of mankind, they are nothing.

The Academy is very much clinically oriented, and we do a disservice not to make it clear that it is. The clinician has an important role in the Academy.

FISHER: I'd like to emphasize one final point, and that is that the American Academy of Optometry is becoming quite international in its scope, too. It's not strictly limited to the United

States. Because I am the "foreigner" around here, I think I
should say that we in Canada are very proud of the Academy.
Actually, there are about 100 members there, and they are very
proud to be able to be members. I think the Academy has done
a great deal to raise the sights of all of us, not only in the United
States but in other countries.

Obviously answers would have been couched in quite different words,
but would the responses of M. Steinfeld, past president in 1922; Carel
Koch, secretary in 1923; and Eugene Wiseman, president in 1923 have
been much different? Their very words quoted in earlier chapters
suggest they would not. The Academy certainly had grown and changed
since its founding, and no doubt administrative reorganization must
occur, but fundamentally the Academy was much the same in terms of
its basic character and the goals it was striving to achieve.

REFERENCES

1. Fitch L. Annual report of president. Am J Optom Arch Am Acad Optom, Jan
   1961;38(1):43-45.
2. From a comment by H. Simmerman. AAO Living History videotape, 1984: AAO
   Archives, ILAMO, St. Louis.
3. Peters HB. The Sections of the American Academy. Am J Optom Arch Am Acad
   Optom, July 1961;38(7):405-409.
4. The Executive Council. Am J Optom Arch Am Acad Optom, Jan 1963;
   40(1)52-54.
5. Three-part Academy meeting. J Am Optom Assn, Nov 1962;34(4):333.
6. The Annual Meeting of 1963 at Chicago. Am J Optom Arch Am Acad Optom,
   Jan 1964;41(1):52-54.
7. Science information program. Am J Optom Arch Am Acad Optom, Jan 1965;
   42(1):40-44.
8. Report of the Science Information Committee. Am J Optom Arch Am Acad
   Optom, Mar 1967;44(3):210-212.
9. The American Academy of Optometry, 1969 Annual Meeting in Philadelphia.
   Optom Wkly, Jan. 15,1970;61(3):210-212.
10. Hirsch MJ. The two-fold aim of the American Academy of Optometry. Optom
    World, Sept 1964;51(9):6-10.
11. Forty-Four Year Accumulative Index of the American Journal of Optometry and
    Archives of the American Academy of Optometry. Chicago: Professional Press,
    1968.
12. Supplement to Am J Optom Arch Am Acad Optom, June 1985;62(6).
13. National visual science information retrieval center. Am J Optom Arch Am Acad
    Optom, Jan 6, 1966;43(1):66-67.
14. Mourning Academy renames post-grad courses. Optom Wkly, Jan 6, 1966;
    57(1):42.
15. The first annual Hofbrau. Am J Optom Arch Am Acad Optom, Jan 1968; 45
    (1):64.

16. A good step toward more effective communications. Optom Wkly, Jan. 25, 1968;59(4):35-36.
17. The Beverly Hilton Meeting of the Academy. Am J Optom Arch Am Acad Optom, Jan 1969;46(1):68-71.
18. Record 450 enroll for Academy Courses, Koch honored for twenty-five years as secretary. Optom Wkly, Jan 4, 1968;59(1):31-33.
19. Fisher EJ. President's report-1969. Am J Optom Arch Am Acad Optom, Jan 1970; 47(1):70-75.
20. American Academy of Optometry. J Am Optom Assn, Oct 1966;37(10):933-952.
21. The American Academy of Optometry. J Am Optom Assn, June 1969;40(6): 624-632.

CHAPTER 7

A Period of
Problems and Challenge
1970–1979

One of the biggest concerns about the activities of the Academy as it entered its sixth decade was the format of the annual meetings. There was a crunch for time created by the huge increase in the number of papers proposed for presentation, the burgeoning volume of material on the six section programs, and the vast array of continuing education courses filling the days. Many of the programs overlapped, with as many as six continuing education courses going on at once. Time for presentation of papers was set very closely and discussion allotted only five minutes. Yet there were more papers and courses proposed than could be squeezed in.

A great deal more research in vision was going on by the 1970s than at any time before. There were many new subjects with proliferation of various types of contact lenses, low vision becoming a significant part of optometric service, sports vision beginning to appear on the scene, fascinating new techniques for detection of ocular pathology, and a general explosion of knowledge in visual science. There were also more optometric educators because several new schools had recently opened, and more faculty members were busy at those in existence because student enrollment was very high. These optometric educators, many with Ph.D. degrees, were carrying on research and needed a place to report it. A great many visual scientists in allied disciplines had discovered the value of the Academy as an excellent forum for reporting their research. Besides that, there was a greater number of members in the AAO, with a higher percentage of them better trained than ever before, and more and more optometrists were presenting significant clinical studies.

Those facts account for the good health of the Academy. They were also the cause of some of its consternation. The Executive Council studied the matter of the format of the annual meetings and considered methods to relieve the pressure on the crowded sessions. A committee was appointed to review the situation and to prepare a questionnaire to obtain the views of the membership.[1] Also considered was the question of whether it was necessary to set up an incorporated, nonprofit educational foundation to meet the requirements of the Internal Revenue Service. This had been discussed before, but now the secretary was authorized to study the necessity of such a foundation.

A Format Analysis Committee, chaired by Henry B. Peters with the help of a specialist in question writing, prepared a set of questions and surveyed attitudes about not only the annual meeting program format but the topics presented and their selection.[2] The key issues being addressed were (1) overlap of various program elements (continuing education, section meetings and general papers program);[*] (2) organization of individual papers into scientific (physiological optics) and clinical (optometry) groupings so that papers on related subjects would be sequenced together; (3) the selection process to improve the quality of papers, particularly since there was an increasing number proposed each year; and (4) the amount of time allocated to each paper (uniform or related to the merit or content of the paper).

Response to the questionnaire was excellent but the information gained did not lead to major format alteration. A few trends were shown, but in general the members felt that the present program pattern was perhaps the best possible. A few of the results: (1) the number of papers being presented was about right; (2) length of meeting should not be extended; (3) most members did not have difficulty understanding the jargon of papers they wanted to understand; (4) level of papers was about right; (5) review of papers should be the same or more rigorous, not less; (6) quality of papers was rated good; (7) more emphasis on clinical papers would please the majority; (8) should be only one meeting per year; and (9) simultaneous presentations acceptable. Thus, evidence indicated that the Academy was doing a good job in meeting the educational needs of its members.

No drastic change in format was made, or perhaps even possible, to alleviate the tight schedule. The program at the 1972 annual meeting in New York City included 123 papers, not counting the presentations at the meetings of the seven sections. Forty-four of the papers were pre-

---

[*] Two papers sessions were run simultaneously, one room used for presentations on clinical subjects and another for basic research papers.

sented by individuals not connected with any optometry school, all but a few of them were on university faculties, and none of them were optometrists themselves. The topics ranged from evaluating the visual status of special children, to functioning of the rods, to biocybernetics, to flicker fusion, to topical anesthetics, to visual illusions and more. What a difference from the first meeting! Even a decade or two or three before, optometrists would never have dreamed that some of those topics would ever appear on the Academy program. The founders of the Academy would no doubt shake their heads in amazement at the practice of optometry dealing with the detailed detection of pathology, in-depth vision therapy, and being on the verge of use of pharmaceutical agents for detection of pathology, with limited use of therapeutical agents not far off.

There were plenty of quality continuing education courses available to cram every minute on the program. Invitations were sent each year to many individuals to propose a course; in fact, any member could do so. The committee then selected those to be presented. The selections were made partly upon the qualifications of the individual, partly upon the topics themselves, but also upon how the subject would fit into a balanced program, one not too heavy in any single topic area. Selection was difficult. For example, in 1972 twice as many proposals were made as could be scheduled. The courses were generally required to be practice-oriented and of a quality acceptable for the continuing education requirements of various state boards. The 122 courses selected for 1972 covered nine areas of professional interest, with four classified as miscellaneous:[3]

Area	Number of Courses
Contact Lenses	29
Refraction & General Optometry	19
Practice Management and Patient Care	18
Pathology	15
Orthoptics and Visual Training	11
Lens Design and Dispensing	10
Learning Disorders	9
Low Vision	4
Pharmacology	3
Miscellaneous	4

The continuing education courses were open to all optometrists, as they had been from the beginning. Attendance by non-Academy members was very good and by this time had reached over fifty percent of the total. The Academy program itself, held after the conclusion of the postgraduate courses, was open only to members and their guests. The section meetings captured most of the interest on the part of the members involved.[4] Papers were presented, but panel discussions were nearly always a part of each program and created the most interest. Discussions were sometimes more heated and more extended following panels than at the more formal paper presentation sessions.

In 1971 the Section on Optometric Education had been added. The membership was limited to optometric educators, hopefully from all the schools of optometry. Each section's committee was to arrange its own program, primarily aimed at discussion of items of mutual interest.[5] At the 1972 annual meeting the Section on Visual Science held its first meeting. It had been suggested to the Executive Council at its meeting in December 1971 by Glenn Fry and Henry Peters. It was authorized by the Executive Council at an interim meeting. It still exists today.

The section programs were a very significant part of the Academy meeting. Each section met from six to ten hours with a large number and variety of topics covered. In 1972 the sections and the numbers of papers presented were as follows: Binocular Vision and Perception, Nathan Flax and William M. Ludlam, co-chairmen — thirty-one presentations; Contact Lenses, Maurice Poster, chairman — thirty-three presentations; Section on Optometric Education, Theodore Grosvenor, chairman — twelve presentations; Section on Pathology, Philip G. Sloan, chairman — twenty-four presentations; Section on Public Health and Occupational Optometry, Louis Warshaw, chairman — twenty-three presentations; Section on Refraction, Dorothy Bergin, chairwoman — twenty-three presentations; and Section on Visual Science, James W. Walters, chairman — sixteen presentations.

Besides the 122 postgraduate courses, the 123 papers in the general program, and the 162 presentations in section meetings, there were two invited papers. Thus, the dilemma of a person attending the Academy meeting was to select from 409 presentations. In case he could not fill his time, there were two banquets, several luncheons, a number of committee meetings, visiting with friends and acquaintances, and sightseeing in the host city. That was in 1972. The program got even busier in the years ahead, with educational exhibits and a poster session added later, which in 1985 numbered forty-eight posters. It is well known that Academy members often do not get much sleep for one week in December.

Awards were becoming an important part of the Academy meeting.[6]

Honorary Life Membership had been granted from time to time beginning in 1947. This honor is awarded to a person who has contributed significantly to the affairs of the Academy. From 1970 on, awards became a quite significant part of the Academy program.

The Charles F. Prentice Medal was established by the Academy in 1958, but it was awarded for the first time in 1963, then 1964 and 1967. It was decided at a joint meeting of the Awards Committee and the Executive Council in 1970 to make the award annually, though later that was not always done. The Prentice Award is made to a scientist, not necessarily an Academy Fellow nor even an optometrist, who has made a significant contribution to the advancement of knowledge in visual science. Nominations for this honor can be made by the officers or the membership at large. The recipient presents a paper during the meeting and the medal is presented at the Round Table Banquet. The first recipient was William A.H. Rushton in 1963.

The Julius F. Neumueller Award was established in 1969 by Neumueller, Professor Emeritus of Physical and Geometrical Optics at Pennsylvania College of Optometry. For his love of optics and his earnest desire to keep this fundamental subject alive in the schools, he set up a sizable trust fund in the Academy, the income from which is to be awarded annually to the undergraduate student who submits the paper judged best by the committee on one of the following subjects: geometrical optics, ophthalmic optics, or optics of the eye. David H. Fox and Peter M. Smith were the first recipients in 1971.

The Glenn A. Fry Award was established in 1970, by the American Optometric Foundation, to honor Glenn Fry, who had contributed so much to optometry through his writings, teaching, and administrative duties at Ohio State University.* The first award was to Anthony Adams and Arthur Affandor for the best paper at the 1970 meeting. Since then it has been awarded to an individual invited to make a presentation. The Papers Program Committee selects the recipient and he is invited to read his paper during the annual meeting.

The Contact Lens Section had been granting certificates since 1948. It started slowly, but as contact lens practice grew, many more optometrists sought diplomate status and the number in the Contact Lens Section increased considerably. The value of this certification had been discussed many times, and it often was pointed out that one important factor was a sense of pride of accomplishment. Attempts to increase the

---

* Several additional awards have been established since 1970, and they are described in more detail in the Appendix.

importance of becoming a diplomate were made in 1973 by Solon Braff, Chairman of the Section:[7]

> "Unfortunately," Dr. Braff said, "the roster of diplomates is often considered a mere patient-referral directory. The emphasis should really be placed upon the importance of identifying the optometrist as a person who is especially proficient in the contact lens field.
>
> "Referral is important," he stated, "but such identification is of greater value to the profession in many other ways. Colleagues must know who can be relied upon, whether they are seeking lecturers for a program, or simply need advice in organizational or personal contact lens matters. Members of the section feel that qualified contact lens specialists have a genuine obligation to make their knowledge a matter of record."

In attempting to focus the profession's attention upon the importance of the diplomate award, Braff noted that to be truly meaningful, every Fellow of the American Academy of Optometry who is completely competent in contact lenses should be recognized. He stated that about sixty percent of the eligible members were already candidates or had completed the requirements.

Other sections had considered certification from time to time. The next one to institute a certification process was the Section on Binocular Vision and Perception. The plan was approved by the Executive Council in December 1971 at Toronto for implementation in December 1972.[8] The prospectus for the establishment of the diplomate program stated:

> The proposed diplomates would be an elite group of optometrists who have demonstrated a high level of theoretical knowledge and practical skills in the art and science of optometric visual training, through a comprehensive written and practical examination in this subject area and submission of case reports to demonstrate sufficient experience and practice in this specialty.

The purposes were to broaden the skills of the diplomates, provide a list of qualified practitioners to third-party payment systems, to develop a referral list, and to increase general education in this field. The procedure for becoming a diplomate was outlined and plans were made to examine ten candidates at the annual meeting in New York City. Of this group, two were certified as diplomates.

A diplomate program in low vision was started one year later. A prospectus was submitted to the Executive Council in December 1972. In this case the diplomate status would be good for only five years, then a recertification would be required. The first examination session was scheduled for San Francisco, December 1973. Randall T. Jose was the Section Chairman. The official records do not show how many were awarded diplomate status at that time; however, that date was the beginning of certification in low vision. *

November 1973 marked the end of an era for the Academy. The death of Carel C. Koch terminated a career of service to the AAO that had lasted half a century. He had been its secretary for thirty-three years and edited its journal for forty-four years. He was without doubt the single most influential individual in the life of the Academy. Those who worked closest with him realized what a great deal of work he did and how effective he was. In 1972 Koch received the Apollo Award from the American Optometric Association for his great service to the profession. Excerpts from eulogies to him describe what he meant to the Academy and its members:

> All who knew him were impressed by his immense knowledge and by his wide experience as a professional man and community leader. One was impressed, perhaps even more, by the vigor of his mind, his enthusiasm, his joviality, his candor, and his simplicity. In fact, we ask ourselves which we admire more — his achievements in the advancement of visual science or his humanity?[9]
>
> His greatest dedication and love was to the development of a truly scientific literature of highest quality for the profession of optometry. The remarkable success of the *American Journal of Optometry* is a testament to his leadership. Through this journal, the profession, its education and its scientific attainments were stimulated to even higher standards of excellence. His personal contributions were monumental and generate a debt we can only repay by continuing his effort.[10]

The Executive Council of the American Academy of Optometry voted to strike a medal in memory of Carel C. Koch. The medal was to be awarded "for outstanding contributions to interprofessional relations," a subject that was always of vital interest and concern to Koch.

---

* Based upon a conversation with Frank Brazelton, who reported several candidates passed the examination at that time.

PRESIDENTS OF THE
AMERICAN ACADEMY OF OPTOMETRY

EDWARD J. FISHER
1969–1970

JOHN ZETTEL
1971–1972

PRESIDENTS OF THE
AMERICAN ACADEMY OF OPTOMETRY

HENRY B. PETERS
1973–1974

GARLAND W. CLAY
1975–1976

FREDERICK J. BAUBLITZ
1977–1978

The medal was created similar in design to the Academy's Charles F. Prentice Medal. On the front side was a profile of Carel and on the reverse side, the Academy seal, a space for the recipient's name and date, and the purpose for the award. "There is no better way to perpetuate the memory of one who was admired and loved by so many."[11] Henry B. Peters was the first recipient in 1974.

Having one person as secretary for a third of a century and having the same headquarters location, and thus the business affairs of the organization handled by the same experienced individual, were tremendous assets to the Academy. Many organizations, particularly in their early years, have had this fortunate experience, as did the AOA with Ernest Kiekenapp as its secretary and journal editor for many years. However, problems can develop when that era comes to a sudden end, at least if a transition to someone else to perform the duties had not already begun.

An assistant secretary, John Schoen, had been appointed in 1967. Koch had relinquished editorship of the *Journal* in 1968; however, he remained as the publisher. Much of the continuity of the Academy operation was represented by Koch himself. He was always there to counsel and to provide answers and suggestions. With that source suddenly gone, it was difficult and took time for other people to carry on and to figure out how to get the work done for which Koch had been responsible.

The Executive Council at the 1973 annual meeting in San Francisco labored hard to resolve the problems. John N. Schoen was elected secretary-treasurer, an office he was to hold for nine years.* His practice was in Owatonna, Minnesota, and the Academy office was moved there. It was also necessary to retain an accountant and an attorney immediately to go over Academy affairs, especially some details of Koch's estate since he was publisher of the *Journal*.

It was decided to purchase the *American Journal of Optometry* from the Koch estate. This also involved purchase of the shares of journal partnership owned by Monroe Hirsch and John Schoen.[12] The name of the journal was changed to the *American Journal of Optometry and Physiological Optics*. A publisher also had to be found once ownership rights had been obtained. A contract was signed with the Professional Press, Inc., of Chicago, publisher of the *Optometric Weekly*. This was all done in a very short time, but no doubt not without some difficulties and

---

* Schoen gave the secretary's report at the 1973 annual meeting, so thus he reported for the secretary;s office ten times.

problems. However, the January 1974 issue was published and the *Journal* continued to appear regularly. This went as smoothly as it did because some planning had been done about how this should be accomplished. Publication by the Professional Press continued through 1975. Beginning in 1976 and since then, it has been published by the Williams and Wilkins Company of Baltimore. *

The question of corporate status of the Academy also arose. It had been incorporated in Washington, D.C., in 1929, but now changes to tax-exempt status were required and certain reports due. Because of this, moving the office, a new secretary taking over, and the *Journal* finding a new publisher, it is no wonder President Henry Peters commented in his 1974 annual report, "It has been a trying period. As you may well surmise, the Executive Council has been a busy group this year." There had been some tentative plans for transition of the secretary's office and purchase of the *Journal*, but the death of both of the principal stockholders within weeks of each other compounded the problems. Still it apparently went quite smoothly, much to the credit of the Executive Council and others involved.[13]

At this time in history, the training of optometric technicians was a hot discussion topic in the profession. Several schools of optometry and some other institutions, generally community colleges, were offering courses for either optometric assistants or optometric technicians. There was concern about whether or not this was proper; the question being, could the use of technicians be unwarranted delegation of professional function and judgment? The issue was more complex than indicated by that simple statement. Involved was the question of whether or not technicians or assistants could attend continuing education courses, either ones designed for them or others designed for optometrists but dealing with a topic of interest in the work of technicians. The Academy had adopted a policy against teaching technicians at its meetings in 1955 and did so again in 1973. This was not the last time this issue would be faced.

The problem of finding a new publisher for the *Journal* and working through the details of the arrangement took much of the time and energy in 1975. Still other Academy activities went on as usual, with membership and attendance at the meetings still growing. The *Journal* continued to publish full issues of high-quality scientific articles, though there were problems catching up with the publication deadlines. A referee system using Academy Fellows had been instituted, and manu-

* The Appendix contains a brief history of the *Journal*.

scripts went through a fine-screening process. Authors were given guidelines for manuscript preparation, and quality steadily improved. The same was true of presentations at the annual meeting. A format was developed for proposal of a paper and for its subsequent publication.

A number of chapters of the Academy were active in the mid-1970s, as many still are a decade later. Some chapters have come and gone, some have had their ups and downs, and a few have functioned actively for many years. The national body encouraged the formation of local chapters and assisted as much as possible, though the encouragement and assistance waxed and waned over the years. The function and formation of chapters were described in July 1977 as follows:[14]

> One purpose of local chapters is to exchange ideas between annual meetings of the Academy. With continuous communications between Fellows, the Academy's objective of furthering the development of optometric sciences is served.
>
> The procedure to obtain a charter for a new chapter is simple. Any ten Fellows in good standing who live within a reasonable distance of one another may apply to the Executive Council to start a chapter. The Executive Council will consider the application and, upon approval of the request, will direct the secretary of the Academy to prepare a charter designating the territory that will be covered by the chapter. When the charter is received the chapter is authorized to begin its official activities.
>
> The new rules of the operation of a chapter are simple and few. Local chapters are required to operate under the Constitution and Bylaws of the Academy. Chapter activities can be as numerous and as varied as necessary to meet the needs of the Fellows. One function that is useful to the Academy is the identification of optometrists who meet the criteria for fellowship. A local chapter can serve to introduce potential members to the Fellows and to the goals of the Academy.

In the early years, the chapters generally were run quite independently from the parent body. Some groups quite likely called themselves "chapters" of the AAO but in reality may never have been approved formally, or if they had been at one time, failed to meet continuing requirements. In some cases, a chapter became inactive for a period of time and then reactivated itself. There is even evidence that in one case the same chapter was chartered three times.

Communication between the chapters and the national body had generally been very poor until the past few years. In recent years, the chairman of a Chapters Committee has made considerable effort to clear up the records and to maintain contact with the chapters. The record as of October 1986 shows that since the first chapter (the Maryland Chapter) in 1929, forty-seven have been chartered, with sixteen active at the present time.[15]*

In 1977 the Academy went abroad. Planning began the year before to hold a meeting in London with the British Chapter as host.[16] The program in general followed the American Academy's program for original papers, twenty minutes in length with five minutes of questions, presented over a three-day period, April 1977. Research departments of the British schools and colleges of optometry were well represented. Clinical papers included several on pediatric optometry, emphasizing case reports and original research for correction of strabismus. Also presented was a provocative evaluation of the results of strabismus surgery. The latest techniques in geriatric optometry were reviewed. An evaluation of a new progressive addition lens was presented. Papers on contact lenses, with special emphasis on soft lenses, formed a large part of the program. Fitting of the Sauflon lens for continuous wear lasting up to three months was discussed. In England, where prescription of contact lenses is subject to less government regulation, clinicians had more opportunity to experiment with soft lenses well in advance of the United States, and this subject created much interest. Papers on teaching methods of optometric educators, both in England and in the United States, were reviewed. Systems of improving effectiveness of teaching by using students' evaluations of their teachers were presented. A particularly provocative paper concerned the development of a computer-based system as an aid in teaching refraction to undergraduate students.

The meeting was well attended by members of the British Chapter of the Academy, and delegates from a total of seventeen countries were registered. This emphasized the need to review the membership requirements as they were applied to optometrists outside of the United States. The problems were largely matters of terminology (whether one must go by the title "optometrist," for example) and prohibition against advertising, office appearance, etc., in other countries. These questions were discussed at length by the Executive Council and with AAO members from other countries. As is always the case when the matter of ethics is discussed, there were wide differences of opinion. Should there be a

* The Appendix contains a brief history of the chapters.

relaxation of high standards of practice which had been a fundamental goal of the Academy from its beginning, because the status of optometry as a profession was different in the various countries?

After the discussions with many delegates, the following decisions were made:[17]

1. The rules regarding the Standards of Conduct be endorsed as they are set forth, not only in the United States, but in all other parts of the world.

2. The Judicial Committee was instructed to prepare a letter advising all members outside the United States, Canada, Great Britain and Ireland of the decision. Enclosed with this letter was a copy of the Constitution and By-laws, as well as the policy pertaining to violations of the Rules of Conduct as contained in the Rules and Regulations of the American Academy.

3. The British Chapter would no longer have, as members, Fellows living in countries outside Great Britain and Ireland. Such members would become members-at-large of the American Academy of Optometry.

4. Following the letter to these members, those not in compliance with the rules would be placed on probation for a period of one year. If at that time, the violations have not been corrected, the member would be suspended for three years. The final step would be expulsion from the Academy.

The final paragraph of the letter sent to all members expressed a basic principle of the Academy, one which would face some very serious challenges in the years ahead.

> The main concern of the Executive Council and the Judicial Committee is that the Academy must continue to represent and encourage the highest standards of practice in the world and that making these decisions will help to do this.

The entire matter of admission to membership was undergoing detailed scrutiny at this time. In December 1976 a committee was appointed by President Frederick Baublitz to review the entire admission procedure and membership standards and to make recommendations. The increased number of applicants was creating a burden in reading their case reports and giving the examination. Of course there was the perennial question as to whether the standards were too high or too low in terms of optometric practice in 1976.

The health-care professions in the 1970s were facing the issues raised by consumers about credentialing for relicensure. Many states had passed laws requiring continuing education to be relicensed. There was consideration of reexamination as well, in order to prove continuing adequate skills to practice. The Academy looked at this issue in regard to membership, having always stood for the highest standards possible and setting membership requirements at a level to achieve them. One of the recommendations of the Ad Hoc Committee on Admissions addressed this issue.

> In attempting to continually improve the delivery of health care by those providing optometric services, the Committee recommends that challenge examinations be conducted periodically by the Academy to test the knowledge and proficiency of clinician Fellows. Those who are successful in passing the examination would be designated a diplomate (for example, in the Primary Care Section) or some other appellate as determined by the Executive Council.

This recommendation further stated that the program should begin on a voluntary basis and eventually become mandatory for continuing fellowship. Relevant courses would be developed and offered at the Academy's annual Continuing Education Program. The Executive Council approved the recommendation of the Ad Hoc Committee and also established an annual Academy Forum on topical issues. Health Manpower Credentialing was chosen as the first forum topic.[18]

The forum was held as planned, but challenge examinations for continuing membership have not as yet been adopted, even though reevaluation is required for diplomate status in some of the sections. Credentialing itself was not a dead issue however. The American Optometric Association had studied it intently for several years. Formation of sections in the AOA had occurred and diplomate status had been discussed. The Academy has also faced the credentialing issue numerous times and no doubt will continue to do so.

A critical issue raised again was whether membership in the American Optometric Association should be required for membership in the Academy, as it had been some years before. On December 9, 1976, the Executive Council voted to "reaffirm the long standing policy that membership in another organization shall not be a prerequisite for Academy membership;* nor shall membership in another organization prohibit Academy membership."[19]

---

* The records do not reveal exactly when membership in the AOA was no longer required for membership in the Academy. An article published in the October 1966

The Ad Hoc Committee on Admissions in December 1977 made a number of recommendations concerning the admissions and examining process.[20] The forty recommendations, a few of which did not deal directly with admissions, were presented by Chairman Melvin Wolfberg. After discussion by the Executive Council, a number of them were adopted, and they became the basis for the present-day admissions brochure. *

Much improvement was made in the procedure, and as Morris Kirschen said in 1986, having been chairman for ten years, "I have seen the metamorphosis from examining candidates in the bedrooms at annual meetings to the present formalized system that has more class."[21]

The latter part of the 1970s saw improvement not only in the revision and formalization of the admission procedures but in the process of obtaining diplomate status in the various sections. The purpose was not necessarily to raise the standards but to clarify the procedures, to make them fair and easy to follow, and to assure adherence to the requirements and to accurately determine the capabilities of the applicants with increasing stress on competence of members.

The sections of the Academy also were busy formalizing their operating procedures, including selection of officers, specification of duties, formation of committees and detailing their functions, and the general format of activity and program operation at the annual meeting. The Executive Council spent a great deal of time going over such matters with the section chairmen and with the annual meeting committee. There was considerable change in the format of the presentations at the annual meeting, much due to the insistence of President Baublitz. As a result there was less competition between the sections, and better program planning made it easier for members to attend the presentations of their choice.

The latter half of the 1970s was a period of formalization and reorganization. Indeed, to some degree restructuring is always true of associations, academies, and clubs of all sorts, but at certain times it becomes more significant than at others. The Carel Koch era of the Academy ended in 1973. It took the next several years to pull things

issue of the *Journal of the AOA* (pp 930-940) clearly states that AOA membership was required. The motion passed in December 1976 states that the policy not requiring membership in any other organization was "long standing."

* The Manual of Procedure for the Committee on Admittance presently published by the Academy describes membership requirements and the admissions process as it stands today.

together — set up a new office, face the many problems of publishing the *Journal,* deal with the financial and legal problems involved — and all at a time when membership was growing and the profession itself was facing a more complicated existence in an atmosphere of changing modes of vision-care delivery, third-party involvement, and government regulation and deregulation.

Academy presidents in this era often referred to the "struggle," the "trying times," the "disarray," and the "salient efforts" to plod through the transition period to a new form of operation for the organization. There were minutes, printed reports, policies described here and there, but the need for continuity of action and a ready source of reference material was becoming highly imperative. The secretary-treasurer, John Schoen, was instructed in 1977 to produce, with the help of the Executive Council and others as needed, a *Manual on Policies.* This was published in March 1978. * It included items related to admissions, budget, awards, the chapters, dues, the *Journal,* the sections, the annual meeting, the Executive Council and more. The bylaws were published separately and had recently been rewritten and revised, not because of many substantial changes but to bring them up to date with present-day operation.

History books are never "best-sellers" because they generally must recite many details which are somewhat dry and routine. Dates, facts, names, places, and numbers must be part of the chronicle. Amending the bylaws is not exciting two decades after it happened. Putting together a policy manual as the Academy did in 1978, important as that act was, is hardly a big reader attention-grabber. But a history of the Academy is not only the recitation of events and facts, it is also a story of the people and their experiences.

The fun, the social activities, the fellowship, the pleasure of travel and all that goes with it is part of Academy life as well. But that segment of Academy life is not recorded in the minutes. In the early years of the Academy, the optometric press, such as *Optometric Weekly, Optical Journal and Review of Optometry,* and several others, published news items about the Academy and many of the personalities involved. Reporters from these magazines attended the meetings and banquets and wrote colorful descriptions of them and of some of the individuals (some are referred to in early chapters of this book). That is rarely done today. The Academy *Journal* publishes little news and there are few

---

* So far as can be determined, this was the first compilation of the policies and procedures in a single publication.

sources reporting the non-business atmosphere of the Academy.*

There is one source of this kind of feeling. A number of "living history" videotapes were produced in 1983 and 1984.** The participants were mostly past AAO presidents, along with several other prominent figures. Their reminiscing about the past adds a flavor to Academy history that can be found nowhere else. They tell of pranks and jokes and various "characters" that they remember — of stories like the time a grand piano was installed in a hotel suite for midnight group singing, of discussions most of the night with colleagues, and of hofbraus and banquets that were too short or too long and with menus that stuck in the memory for one reason or another. They flavored many concepts about events and people and reasons for actions that written words cannot convey. But most of all they made it clear that there was more value to belonging to the Academy than business and education alone.

So the personal experiences — renewing acquaintances, heated discussions, dining at choice restaurants, keeping the midnight hours, swapping tales and stories, reliving the good old college days, making new friends, and just plain enjoying being in optometry — went on at every Academy meeting and at the committee and Executive Council meetings as well. Like the time — two members arrived late for an Executive Council dinner but still had to help pay the bill — and many more "rememberable" happenings. Such memories pervade this entire story of the Academy, though they are not spread in print through all of its pages.

But very serious business lay ahead in 1978. The U.S. Federal Trade Commission (FTC) had outlawed prohibitions against advertising optometric services and ophthalmic materials. This struck at a very vital principle of the Academy — the requirement that members not be allowed to advertise. In fact, it represented a threat to membership restrictions based upon factors other than competence. This created a quandary as to what action to take or whether to continue with present practice standards and face a possible lawsuit by the FTC.

The AOA had filed a suit requesting the courts to vacate the FTC ruling. What the Academy should do depended partly upon the outcome of that suit. Even though, at the time, it may not have been

---

* In 1977 the idea of publishing a separate quarterly bulletin was considered but rejected.
** The individuals who appeared on the videotapes were J. Donald Kratz, Melvin Wolfberg, Harold Simmerman, William Feinbloom, Bradford Wild, Edward J. Fisher, Daniel G. Hummel, Boyd J. Eskridge, Robert Bannon, Don Springer, Irvin Borish, Henry Peters, Ralph Wick, and Meredith Morgan.

apparent how serious this situation would become or how profound the effect would be on the AAO, action was taken to avoid undesirable complications as far as possible. In December 1978, the Executive Council voted to set aside the provision in its bylaws prohibiting advertising by members, and determined that appropriate revision be delayed pending decisions in the cases involving the FTC. But this was only the beginning, and the nature of the Academy was going to undergo some significant alteration in the years ahead.

The issues of membership requirements, certification of continuing competence, credentialing of optometric specialties, diplomate programs, and even residencies were high on the list of concerns as the 1970s came to a close. President Brad Wild put the issues very clearly and well described the Academy's aims and purposes in his report to the Fifty-Eighth Annual Meeting in Anaheim, California, December 9–11, 1979:[22]

> Of great concern to the Academy are the regulations of the Federal Trade Commission. The regulations specifically prohibit any form of discrimination based on advertising. As you know the prohibition of advertising is one of the items of the code of conduct for all Academy Fellows. The authority of the FTC is currently being challenged in the courts. Until this matter is resolved legal counsel has advised us that it will be necessary to refrain from enforcing this portion of our code of conduct. However we are confident that all Academy Fellows will continue to adhere to our traditional tenents of practice despite the necessity of dropping, hopefully temporarily, the enforcement of the prohibition of advertising from our code of conduct.
>
> A challenge that faces the Academy is in the field of certification. Let me call it to your attention. The Academy has customarily prided itself on its progressive attitudes toward education and professional competence. The Executive Council will consider the concept of certifying continuing competence on a regular basis. A second challenge is in the field of certification of the optometric specialties. Residencies in a variety of optometric subspecialties already exist. The organization of the Academy has already evolved into a number of groupings that we call sections. Now we have approved diplomating programs for a number of these sections and are considering other diplomate programs. These diplomates have been

recognized by at least one state as evidence that the individual, the Diplomate, possesses special competence in the field of diplomation. This fact appears to imply that the Academy is leading the way in the identification of optometric specialties and that, as a result of this identification, educational programs, perhaps residencies, may develop in these fields.

The actions of the Federal Trade Commission of course applied to other health professions as well as optometry. It made all of the groups with restrictive ethical standards for membership look like bad guys. Amazingly enough, another report published by the FTC at the same time made Academy members look like good guys. The quality of vision care was studied by the FTC based upon specific criteria the agency adopted. Various practitioners around the nation were then rated as to how their service related to the standards. Quality of care was found lowest among those who advertised nationally, next lowest with local advertisers, better with non-AOA non-advertisers, next with the AOA members, and top quality with Academy members.[23]

What a paradox! The entire matter of evaluating quality of care and even fee levels is a very complex one, but if the findings were reasonably accurate, the evidence indicated that Academy members were producing highest-quality vision care. Yet the Academy was being asked, or even more realistically being required, by the FTC to accept advertising as a standard of practice, yet that had been shown to be a trait of those producing the lowest-quality care.

It was obvious that the Academy faced some troublesome issues in the 1980s.

REFERENCES

1. A few notes on Executive Council actions. Am J Optom Arch Am Acad Optom, Jan 1971;48(1):94-95.
2. Peters HB. Report of the Format Analysis Committee. Am J Optom Archives Am Acad Optom, Apr 1972;49(4):378-388.
3. American Academy of Optometry Ellerbrock Memorial continuing education courses. J Am Optom Assn, Oct 1972;43(11):1189.
4. The 1971 Annual Meeting of the American Academy of Optometry. Optom Wkly, Jan 13, 1972;63(2):48-52.
5. Section on Optometric Education. Am J Optom Arch Am Acad Optom, Jan 1972; 49(1):72.
6. Perry JD. Academy awards. Am J Optom Arch Am Acad Optom, July 1971;48(7): 609-610.
7. Clarifies Academy diplomates. Optom Wkly, May 10, 1973;64(19):466.

8. Ludlam WM, Flax N. A prospectus for the establishment of a diplomate in visual training and orthoptics of the Section on Binocular Vision and Perception. Am J Optom Arch Am Acad Optom, Mar 1972;49(3):271-274.

9. Rosenbloom A. Carel C. Koch, O.D. J Am Optom Assn, Jan 1974;45(1):91-92.

10. Peters HB. Dr. Carel B. Koch, Nov. 23, 1896 -Nov. 3, 1973. Am J Optom Arch Am Acad Optom, Nov. 1973;50(11):850-851.

11. Perry JD. The Carel C. Koch Memorial Medal. Am J Optom Physiol Opt, July 1974;51(7):509.

12. Peters HB. The end of an era. Am J Optom Physiol Opt, Jan 1974;51(1):118-120.

13. Hirsch MJ. Journal has new publisher. Am J Optom Physiol Opt, Jan 1976; 53(1):48-49.

14. Wild BW. Function and formation of Academy Chapters. Am J Optom Physiol Opt, July 1977;54(7):501-502.

15. Published list of chapters as of Oct 1986. AAO Archives, ILAMO, St. Louis, Mo.

16. Wick RE. The Academy went to London. Am J Optom Physiol Opt, June 1977; 54(6):399-400.

17. A letter to members from John Zettel, Jr. Judicial Chairman, attached to the Apr 1977 Minutes of the Executive Council.

18. Wolfberg MD. Academy forum on health manpower credentialing. Am J Physiol Opt, Aug 1978;55(8):531.

19. Minutes of Executive Council, Dec 9, 1976, Portland, Ore.

20. Minutes of Executive Council, Dec 9, 1977, Birmingham, Ala.

21. Letter to author, Dec 1986.

22. Report of President Wild, Annual Meeting, Anaheim 1979. Archives, ILAMO, St. Louis, Mo.

23. Minutes of Executive Council, Dec 6, 1979, Anaheim, Ca.

CHAPTER 8

The Modern Academy 1980–1986

I t is probable that at no time in its history did the Academy begin to look as hard at itself as it did in the early 1980s. This was not entirely by its own choice. The U.S. Federal Trade Commission, as part of its investigation of membership restrictions of various organizations, was beginning to put pressure on the Academy to revise its membership standards.[1] The resulting change has drastically affected the Academy's image in the minds of some people. But most have accepted the new procedures as necessary to conform to the present-day sociological environment.

But the FTC action was not the only reason for critical self-analysis. The average growth of nearly ten percent in membership each year, along with a huge increase in all its educational, publishing, and administrative activities, was causing the officers, and many members as well, to recognize that further reevaluation, reorganization, and revitalization were essential. Then, too, a variety of legal issues was becoming agonizingly complex.

The pressures for change by the 1980s were great, and indeed many still are. It became necessary to seek extensive legal, financial, and management advice. No longer could the Academy function primarily without a paid professional staff. Recordkeeping would have to become more extensive and communication with members much improved. The fundamental goals of the Academy were still the same but they would have to be reached by a somewhat different route.

President Bradford Wild pointed this out in an editorial published in November 1979.[2] He reiterated that the objectives of the Academy were to promote the art and science of vision care by (1) initiating and supporting, in suitable centers and institutions, research and educational programs in optometry and related sciences; (2) affording an

127

opportunity for the presentation and discussion of the results of research in vision; (3) encouraging exceptional and instructive conditions encountered in the practices of individual Fellows; and (4) disseminating knowledge through the *American Journal of Optometry and Physiological Optics*. The next decade, he stated, would require adjustment in Academy activities because of the changing character of the profession.

The biggest problem by far was the matter of compliance with the "law of the land." The U.S. Supreme Court ruled that advertising by practitioners that met legal requirements could not be used as a prohibition for membership in professional societies. In fact, state laws that prohibited advertising professional services and ophthalmic materials, as well as their price, were attacked. When the question first arose, the Executive Council of the Academy voted in December 1978 to set aside the bylaws prohibiting advertising by members. The matter of suspension of the bylaws had not been voted on by the membership, and the action by the Executive Council was later determined to be invalid. Thus it was automatically rescinded, and the prohibition against AAO members' advertising was restored.

It became apparent that elimination of the advertising prohibition and certain other ethical standards would be necessary. This was strongly opposed by some members. The very foundation of the AAO had been laid in adherence to higher standards of practice than required by law, and perhaps even conformed to by the average performance of the profession. Most professional associations and academies had similar standards at that time. All such so-called restrictions were subject to FTC action at the beginning of the 1980s. The AAO had not as yet even been addressed directly by the FTC. The Academy's action in suspending the bylaws had only been an attempt to avoid problems and conform to what would be acceptable membership requirements in the eyes of the government.

Once it became obvious the AAO bylaw prohibition against advertising would have to be enforced unless suspended or changed by vote of the membership, steps were taken to institute the proper procedure to amend the bylaws to conform to state and federal legal requirements. In January 1981, President Merton Flom appointed a committee to study all Academy documents alluding directly or indirectly to advertising and to suggest changes in wording so that Academy policy on advertising would not be in violation of the U.S. Supreme Court decisions or the First Amendment to the U.S. Constitution. The Committee consulted with legal and ethics experts and reviewed scores of relevant documents, including those from other organizations such as the American Medical

Association, American Psychological Association, and the Hastings Institute of Society and Ethics.

The proposed bylaws changes were sent to the membership in advance of a vote as required, with an explanation for them:[3]

> After the U.S. Supreme Court decisions that organizations cannot prevent their members from advertising (in accord with freedom of speech guaranteed under the First Amendment to the Constitution), the Academy's legal counsel recommended that Article III (pertaining to Standards of Conduct in our Bylaws) be carefully studied and completely rewritten, omitting entirely any attempt to prohibit or discourage advertising, except that which is false, fraudulent, deceptive, or misleading. Many members of the Academy and the Council believe these court decisions compromise the premises upon which the Academy was founded and chartered. The Council considered the options available to the Academy — such as challenging the decisions — and decided to propose new language for our Constitution, Bylaws, and other Academy documents (such as the membership application and pledge) stressing the commitment of Academy members to the highest standards of ethics and professional competence.

The President's Newsletter of November 16, 1981, explained the need to understand the changes and at the same time described a bit of history and philosophy of the Academy's position on membership standards:[4]

> If there was a time for understanding within the Academy, now's the time. The proposed changes in the Academy's Constitution and Bylaws are *not* intended to reverse the course charted for the Academy by its founders when they met in the Planter's Hotel in St. Louis on January 11, 1922.
>
> Today the Academy faces potential legal action for its *total* prohibition of advertising by its applicants and members. Our alternatives are to challenge the court decisions (at great expense with negligible chance of winning) or to replace the wording in our Bylaws that prohibits *all* advertising and specific related activities (such as store locations and cash registers.)
>
> We have nearly 60 years of Academy history and tradition as the basis for formulating Bylaw language that describes in *broad and positive terms* the standards of conduct for Academy mem-

bers. Of the five Sections (each a sentence long) in the *proposed* Article III on Standards of Conduct, the first four deal with maintaining the highest standards of the profession, responsible and complete care of patients, maintaining the highest degree of professional competence, and personal standards of behavior not interfering with professional responsibilities.

The most timely issue is covered by the proposed fifth Section that states:

> "The professional standards of members of the Academy require that public statements, announcements of services, and promotional activities provide sufficient information to aid the consumer in making informed judgements and choices, emphasize professional services, and not be deceptive, fraudulent, misleading, or sensational."

This proposed bylaw stresses the heavy responsibility placed upon members for their *public statements, announcements,* and *promotional activities.*

The Academy never has and does not now approve of advertising. Indeed, it is proposed to add to our Constitution *another objective* (Article 11) of "Enhancing the commitment of Academy members to the highest ethical and professional standards of practice." Thus, the objectives of the Academy are scientific, educational, *and professional.*

A special time was set aside at the Sixtieth Annual Meeting in Orlando, Florida, for discussion and vote on the new constitution and bylaws. By no means did all members agree to the amendments, and there was some strong difference of opinion. A few members felt adoption of the new rules would change the basic direction of the Academy. *
The membership voted about seventy-five percent for and twenty-five percent against approval of the new constitution and bylaws.[5]

The Executive Council also promulgated a set of *Guidelines for Public Statements and Information.* These were designed to describe the nature of public announcements and statements, such as advertising, to be false, fraudulent, deceptive, misleading, or sensational. These guidelines and the constitution and bylaws were published and distributed to the membership in 1982.[6] The Admissions Committee and the Judicial

---

* Though from the short perspective of half a decade it may be too early to judge, that prediction has not come true and the quality of the Academy has not declined. That statement does not imply approval of advertising by optometrists; it is only an observation of apparent fact.

Council began to function based upon those documents. But that was not the end of concern about the FTC and its activities in the organization's membership area; in a way it was only the beginning of more serious action by the federal agency.

When the first implication of a possible challenge to the requirements for membership developed, Academy leaders recognized a need to address matters of standards and competence, realizing perhaps that quality would depend in the future to some degree upon voluntary adherence to ethical tenets rather than mandatory rules. No doubt with this in mind, an Academy Forum was held at the annual meeting in Chicago in 1980. The introductory paper, entitled "The Academy and the Future: Introduction — A Tradition At Risk," was presented by Frank Brazelton. A few of his remarks clearly set the stage. Referring to the founders of the Academy in the 1920s, he said:[7]

> Yet there were a few who saw what optometry must do to justify its continuance and its independence. If we are surprised and gratified that such a nucleus of visionaries existed, we should be astonished at how perceptive and accurate their vision proved to be. The principles which they adopted and which still appear in the constitution of this Academy are few, simple, and as relevant now as at any time in the last two generations.
>
> What the founders said in those brief sentences I quoted to you is simply this: that if we wish to earn and maintain respect for our services, we must demonstrate that those services are as good as they can be. Seeing that our patients are well served is a duty that rests on each of us as individuals. Each of us is optometry to our patients and each of us must meet the challenge of rendering efficient, compassionate, and conscientious care in his or her own way.

In alluding to a tradition at risk he said:

> There are critics both in and outside of the Academy who question whether we are viable or relevant to optometry today. This Forum is designed to be an exercise in introspection and so we must look at what the critics say. I will simply pose the issues rather than discuss them or try to respond to them. I hope that you are stimulated to think about them, both during this Forum and afterward.
>
> The questions that I have posed do not present threats of

immediate extinction to the Academy. We are not forced to fashion an emergency response or even a strategy for dealing with them. They simply ask us to look at ourselves seriously and critically. If we can find out and agree what we are and what we're for, then those who must guide this Academy through its next 60 years will know what they must do to preserve and enhance that tradition which we proudly share today.

On the same forum, Melvin Wolfberg spoke on "The Academy and Competence," concluding:[8]

There is little question of the growing acceptance for developing measurements of competence in our society. The bottom line is that the American Academy of Optometry must continue to seek more effective mechanisms for accomplishing these goals. Such activity is clearly in the public interest. The fact that this is a controversial issue has not deterred the Academy from the leadership role it has assumed in the past. It should not deter us now or in the future.

Speaking on professionalism, Irvin Borish concluded:[9]

In the final analysis, our primary concern should not be with rules which threaten punishment to nonconformers. Our primary concern should be to develop and demonstrate a code based upon that which we know is good and right, and upon those visible indicators which assure the public that we are responsible professionals. This code is a goal towards which we must aspire, both as individuals and as a group.

The words of those individuals eloquently describe the beliefs and philosophy of the Academy sixty years after its founding, and few if any of its members would disagree. However, the Federal Trade Commission was not convinced that the Academy was acting in the best interest of the public and optometrists as individuals, this in spite of the changes that had been made amending the constitution and bylaws.

Two documents (Interpretation of the Standards of Conduct and the Guidelines for Public Statements and Information) had been circulated to the membership and their contents approved at the annual meeting, December 1982. Thus the intent and purpose of membership standards and conduct were spelled out in detail. Certainly they were broader than those in effect prior to that time and, in the opinion of legal advice obtained by the Executive Council, were adequate to meet the legal requirements of the day. However, the FTC was not so sure.

On November 29, 1984, the Academy received notice that the FTC's Bureau of Competition was conducting a preliminary non-public investigation into whether the AAO was restraining truthful advertising and use of certain contractual arrangements and business formats by optometrists.[10] All documents relating to solicitation of members, the constitution and bylaws and the various guidelines and interpretive statements, and materials relating to membership requirements were requested by the FTC for review and evaluation.

As can be imagined, this was not received with great joy. On the other hand much had been done to comply with legal requirements. There were meetings, phone calls and much correspondence between various Academy leaders, its administrative officers, attorneys, and many others. Choices were to (1) comply and send the material as requested, (2) withhold some, (3) refuse to comply at all, or (4) mount some counter challenges. Since the Academy had already made adjustments in an attempt to achieve compliance, on advice of counsel and in accordance with the opinion of the majority, it seemed wisest to cooperate fully with the FTC.

As such things usually go, there were further exchanges of information, meetings with representatives of FTC, and long hours of discussion. It was determined that the matter could be adequately settled by a consent degree. This involved the Academy making some changes in its constitution and bylaws in regard to standards, in the Guidelines for Public Statements and Information, and in the Interpretation of Standards. Actually these changes were in general not substantive and involved primarily a clarification of wording in these documents that had been revised only a short time before. Some negotiations were involved, but ultimately a few amendments were agreed upon by the Executive Council and acceptable to the FTC. The proposed changes were sent to the membership in October 1985 for vote at the December annual meeting, at which time the amendments were approved.*

The consent agreement with the FTC involved more than amendment of the documents. The Academy also had to agree to certain conditions in performance and application of the rules and procedures, including a report of how it had complied, making available evidence of compliance and reporting periodically to the FTC. The complete

---

* During much of this period of negotiation with the FTC, Melvin Wolfberg was Academy president. As AOA president, 1969–1970, and during his years on the AOA Board of Trustees, he had gained considerable experience in dealing with governmental agencies and the legal affairs of optometry, and this proved very useful.

documents involved in the agreement with FTC are in legalese, but a synopsis of the consent agreement was published in October 1986 in the *Journal*[11] and can be found in the Appendix.[12]

The Committee on Admissions and the Judicial Committee were in a constant dilemma, with rules and regulations concerning membership requirements fluctuating because of the temporary suspension of certain of the bylaws, their reinstatement, adoption of a new set of membership admission requirements, their revision to suit the FTC, and all of the uncertainties and complexities involved in the routine processing of applications and dealing with violations of the rules by members, though the latter were few in number. This went on for nearly ten years prior to the final agreement with the FTC. Morris Kirschen was chairman of the Admissions Committee all of that time and he, along with many other AAO members who served on the committee, put in countless hours trying to keep up with changing events and in developing a system for fair and efficient review of applications for membership.

The growing number of applicants, along with the increase in the sophistication of the application processing and the oral examination of candidates, made the procedure very time consuming. Even if there had been no change in membership standards, a revamping of the admission process was essential. For several decades the admissions process had functioned on an informal and personal basis with little change. There were four, then later five, regional admissions committees, but formalization of the procedures was needed. The oral examinations were generally given at the annual meeting on a demand basis, in the bedroom of the chairman's suite, rather than at a time certain.

The function of the Committee on Admittance and the requirements for membership were described by Chairman Harold Simmerman in 1966.[13] As he pointed out, at no time has the Academy promoted membership campaigns to increase its size, because in a scientific and educational society, such procedures frequently lead to a large segment of disappointed and undesirable members. Associating oneself as a Fellow of the Academy was entirely on a voluntary basis, and because membership is such a coveted, valued, and highly desirable objective, no further motivation should be needed to keep the membership growing. Still the admissions process should be as smooth as possible to encourage applications and reduce frustrations. Thus frequent review was essential.

The introspection of Academy activities and the administration in the latter 1970s and beginning 1980s was directed at the admissions process as well. During the days of FTC turmoil, the Admissions Committee maintained a low profile concerning the application of rules that were being questioned. Applicants were informed as much as possible as to what the situation was and why there were uncertainties. The process went remarkably well in view of the varying circumstances. At the same time the committee itself was completely reorganized.

The number of committees in the admission process and the number of members were increased. More members were added to the five regional committees. Their functions, responsibilities, and procedures were spelled out in detail, and communications between the chair, the Academy officers, and committee members increased. The greater administrative capability of the Academy, particularly with the move to an office in Washington, D.C., improved the recordkeeping and application processing functions of the Admissions Committee. This was essential with as many as 200 applications per year being submitted.

Admissions Committee reorganization also included the establishment of four special committees. A committee on admissions of members from foreign countries was set up to handle all applications from outside the United States except Great Britain.* Optometric practitioners in the federal service were interested in membership in increasing numbers, and a special committee was revitalized to handle their applications. Scientists and educators had to be evaluated on a different basis than clinicians, and a committee was designed to handle their applications based upon a specific set of guidelines. Then there were some individuals who did not fit properly into any of the other categories, so a committee for administrators and special categories was established in 1985 to evaluate such cases.

A new *Manual of Procedures* for the Committee on Admittance was published for use of all committee members. It contains an admissions process flowchart and all of the details involved in handling an application, all of the necessary documents including the constitution and bylaws, interpretation of the standards of conduct and descriptions of the type of case reports and/or published articles that are desirable, along with the sample letters and forms used in the process. That document, in itself, proves what a far cry obtaining membership in the

---

* The Academy chapter in Great Britain handles its own admissions procedure and makes recommendations for membership directly to the Executive Council. In 1986 the name of the present British chapter of the American Academy of Optometry was changed to the British Academy of Optometry.

PRESIDENTS OF THE
AMERICAN ACADEMY OF OPTOMETRY

Bradford W. Wild
1979–1980

Merton C. Flom
1981–1982

PRESIDENTS OF THE
AMERICAN ACADEMY OF OPTOMETRY

GORDON G. HEATH
1983–1984

MELVIN D. WOLFBERG
1985–1986

FRANK A. BRAZELTON
1987–

Academy is from the early days, when talking to the right person was about all that was required. But more than that, it is a testimonial to the high standards the AAO has achieved, not only in its membership qualifications but in the manner in which it evaluates them. The examinations are held at the annual meeting on an appointment basis and in a dignified manner by committee members who are qualified to do so.

CREDENTIALING

Even though matters of membership requirements settled down to the satisfaction of most members, the topic of credentialing and diplomate status remained a controversial issue. The same subjects were being debated by other professional organizations and in legislative bodies as well. Though not everyone agreed continuing competency to practice should be evaluated, the toughest problem was determining how to measure it fairly and efficiently. The American Optometric Association was studying the same issue, and the question arose as to which organization, AOA or AAO, should carry on this function. Representatives from each met to consider the matter of certification.[14] The AOA had formed sections, but there were no certification requirements for membership and no diplomate status, as was the case of assessing the competence of applicants, and President Flom pointed out in his 1982 report that this was receiving continuing study.[15] The National Board of Examiners in Optometry was retained in April 1981 to study and develop a competency assessment program. Flom explained that action on this matter would proceed slowly and cautiously.

A Long-Range-Planning Task Force of the AOA had reported, among other items, on continuing education, competency assessment, and certification of specialties which were of considerable concern to the Academy. This was an agenda item at the December 1983 meeting of the Executive Council, and an excerpt from the minutes rather succinctly describes the situation as perceived at that time.[16]

> There was considerable discussion of what would happen to the diplomate programs were a new format of specialty certification to be developed. In the course of the conference with AOA Representatives Bucar, Scholles, Tumblin, Ferris and Hunter, Council members expressed the position that Academy fellowships, or section diplomates, for that matter, do not constitute certificates of specialization. Academy diplomates are knowledge based, not competency centered at present. Acad-

emy governance, including the Sections, might usefully inter-act with agents in the field concerning these issues through exchange of position papers although the Executive Council is the agent that authorizes policy for the Academy. When inter-acting with elements in the field of these issues, Sections or individuals affiliated with the Academy should clearly differen-tiate between personal or Section opinions and official Acad-emy policy.

That was by no means the last word on the issues involved. Indeed both AOA and AAO have continued to consider them at length. So the 1980s have been, and may well continue to be, the period of assessment of credentialing and development of plans to take whatever steps are appropriate to the best interests of both the public and the profession in this process.

ADMINISTRATION

Even though the problems of membership standards and all of the complexities of satisfying the FTC regulations consumed time and energy, business for the Academy went on as usual, only there was a lot more of it. The administration of the Academy as it was handled in the 1970s could not keep up with the computerized 1980s. The need for new methods of operation and employment of professional administrators did not happen overnight but became imperative by 1980.

Realizing that the burden of housekeeping affairs was becoming too great to be handled by a practicing optometrist on a part-time basis, even with an office staff employed by the Academy, the Executive Council began to study the situation in 1979. A meeting was held in Owatonna, Minnesota, and the office operation was reviewed.[17] As a result, some staff assignments were readjusted and additional service provided for, but from then on, a plan to establish a permanent headquarters in a major city began to develop.

The Academy did not intend to get into politics nor public relations activities, though it had been involved in the latter some years before. A committee was appointed to study the administrative organization and make recommendations in relation to achieving the goals of the AAO. A preliminary report was presented in April 1981. Excerpts from that report cogently describe the needs and considerations involved:[18]

> We believe the Academy must create a full-time administra-tive position if its activities are to expand beyond the present level. Potential of the Academy to fulfill its tripartite mission —

education, research, and professionalism — is great, but the present organization which depends heavily on volunteers is taxed to maintain the Academy's four current operations: the *Journal*, admissions, continuing education, and the annual papers sessions. Even if Academy programs continue to be limited to these, it is felt that the effectiveness of the Executive Council, and others who perform crucial roles, could be enhanced significantly through the services of a full-time association executive.

The first responsibility of the Executive Council in this decision making process is to determine what directions the Academy is to take in serving its mission. Continuation of present programs with some increase in the current rate of membership growth, and continuing improvement of programs, represents the absolute minimum. Maximum potential defies the imagination, but might include:

> Establishing major vision research awards; supporting vision research projects; organizing continuing education nationally; development of formal course series leading to certificates of completion in specific areas of practice; serving as optometry's voice in matters of national research policy and procedures affecting vision research; interacting with other groups inside and outside the profession which are involved in research education; and professionalism — enhancing the image of optometry as a science-based, serving profession. All of these and more are within the scope of the Academy's mission.

Further consideration of all aspects of the matter led to the conclusion that the best arrangement would be to share offices with some other organization where staff and equipment might be used by both. Cost saving would be one advantage, but the access to experienced staff would be another. Several cities were considered, St. Louis being one because the AOA headquarters was there. Several schools of optometry were also considered as a possible location for office space. It soon became apparent for a number of reasons, mostly spelled out by the ad hoc committee's report as to what programs the Academy might pursue, that Washington, D.C. would be the wisest choice. The third report of the committee presented organizational options, costs, and specific proposals received from several organizations for sharing facilities. The Executive Council accepted the proposal from the National Board of

Examiners in Optometry (NBEO). The plan called for separate and shared space and resources, with Academy activities being handled by its own administrative secretary.

A three-year contract was signed with the NBEO for the establishment of an office in Washington. The transition to the Washington office and the reassignment of functions took several more months than planned, but by mid-1982, the Academy's address was Washington, D.C. The first administrator was Norman Wallis, who had previously been president of Pennsylvania College of Optometry. New facilities and enhanced administrative capability were a great boon to the Academy. Its service and function improved considerably and many volunteers were freed from routine clerical functions.

In April 1984, the NBEO notified the Academy that it would not be able to continue the relationship beyond the end of the current three-year period for various reasons, based on the administrative needs of the National Board and the fact that the space that the Academy was occupying would have to be returned to the landlord of the building under the provisions of the sub-lease arrangement. The Executive Council considered a proposal from Professional Advancement International, a management and development firm located in the same building as the National Board, which specialized in providing full-scope administrative and management services to small and medium-sized professional scientific societies similar to the Academy. The proposal detailed the services to be offered, and the Executive Council, after careful study, accepted the offer. The Academy headquarters was in the same building in a different suite, but otherwise its administration continued much as usual.

Much more had been done in the past few years as well as move the office and employ a management firm. The minutes of the Executive Council meetings, describing the vast range of details with which it had to deal, were reviewed, rewritten (subsequently approved by the Executive Council), and numbered in such a manner as to be more accessible. Extensive and accurate minutes were a necessity for clear evidence of actions taken and policies established. Experience with the FTC had emphasized the importance of the records as well as many other legal and financial ramifications with which any such organization had to deal at this point in time. Liability was a concern also.

Legal counsel advised that adequate insurance must be maintained for officers and everyone acting for the organization. Complexities, ramifications, implications, and complications were many times greater than when the Academy began only a few decades ago. Operating the organization was "big business" in a sense; certainly it had to be operated like a responsible business. The general concept was put well by President Gordon Heath in his report for the year 1983, after having commented that the Academy seemed to be operating much as usual.[19]

> To those of us behind the scene, however, the year has been anything but tranquil as many changes, some initiated in the previous year or two and others begun this year, have been implemented and consolidated to make your Academy a more smooth and efficient operating organization. Over the years, the Academy has functioned in large part by custom and tradition developed and followed by persons holding long-term responsibility for various Academy activities. In too many cases neither the customs and traditions nor the policies and procedures governed by them were ever recorded. Thus, when responsibilities were shifted to new appointees, the lack of clear guidelines, policies, and directions became glaringly apparent and often imposed an undesirable additional burden of discovery or invention on the persons accepting those responsibilities. Your Executive Council has undertaken steps to remedy these problems by developing two major documents: (1) a comprehensive Policy Manual summarizing and codifying all of the official actions of the Council in its various meetings, and (2) an Administrative Procedures Manual covering the operational steps for Academy functions such as Admittance, Annual Meetings, Continuing Education, Section Diplomating and committee activities.

By the mid-1980s the Academy was functioning in a much more businesslike manner. Demands on the time of the Executive Council had reached the point that members had to conduct business almost constantly during the annual meetings. Now a great deal of the business was transacted at mid-year meetings and members had time to attend paper sessions and sectional programs during the annual meetings. Discussions are held to an appropriate time schedule, more work is done by committees, and the actions and records are kept in an orderly fashion. The increased staff support also has been a very significant factor in streamlining the business functions of the Academy.

In spite of the FTC, the Academy was able to begin to carry on some long-range planning. President Melvin Wolfberg describes it in his 1985 annual report:[20]

Organizational planning is a continuing and extremely important responsibility of the Executive Council; a formal session dealing solely with future planning had not been held since 1979. In order to prepare adequately for the future, the Executive Council held a three-day planning session in September of this year. President-Elect Brazelton served as the coordinator and moderator of this event.

The meeting was divided into three segments, namely

1. Goals and objectives
2. Operations and activities
3. Logistics and support

A memorandum summarizing the discussions and conclusions has been disseminated only to the meeting attendees. It is anticipated that after the review of statements and conclusions where a consensus was reached these matters will be referred to appropriate Academy committees, councils, sections, and individuals for follow-up study and/or implementation. Planning subjects included (but were not limited to):

The future role of the Academy in research and education.

The future role of Academy sections.

The role of the *American Journal of Optometry and Physiological Optics.*

The Academy's commitment to professionalism and to professional competence.

The admittance process.

The size of the Academy (membership).

The role of Academy chapters.

The composition of the Executive Council.

Each AAO president finishes his term of office concluding that the organization has made progress and accomplished much, and indeed it has. He also points out there is still more to be done, and that is always true. President Wolfberg did the same when he concluded his term in 1986 with a prediction of great progress in the years ahead.

The Academy had members in some twenty-eight countries outside the United States and membership had grown to 3,274, counting all of the membership categories in 1986. Attendance at the continuing education program at the annual meeting totaled 1,279 in that year. Scientific exhibits had been added in 1984. Interest had also been generated by the special membership categories. The enlarged awards program and enhanced candidate testing and diplomate certification procedures were also an important part of the modern Academy. It had a much different look when Frank Brazelton became its president on January 1, 1987, than when it was founded sixty-five years ago.

THE PROFESSION OF OPTOMETRY AND SIXTY-FIVE YEARS OF THE AMERICAN ACADEMY OF OPTOMETRY

In 1922 optometry was barely in its teens as a licensed profession, still struggling with its commercial origin in jewelry stores and opticians' shops. The issues then were survival, autonomy, and recognition as a profession by its peer disciplines and the public. Those who founded the Academy were both idealists and realists. Their idealism is reflected in the goals they set for the fledgling organization: to promote research and education, and to practice excellence. They understood that optometry could not exist or progress without a firm scientific base of knowledge and technical skills, and the means to make them readily available to the practitioner. But they knew as well that perception determines reality. Would the public, academia, or peer professionals give credence to practitioners who operated like shopkeepers? To be recognized as professionals, optometrists had to behave like professionals, and so the bylaws of the Academy put stringent limitations on commercial setting, display or self-promotion. Their wisdom was justified by the results. The Academy set a standard which the profession at large began to follow in increasing numbers. It was a long, hard struggle, but great strides were made. Consider only the highlights of what the profession has attained in the past sixty-five years as they relate to Academy objectives:

In Education and Research

- Optometric education has developed from two university-based programs, plus a constantly changing number of independent and proprietary schools, to the current sixteen institutions, all but five of which are university-based and all of which are acknowledged by their regional accrediting associations as well as the Council on Optometric Education.

- From two years or less, without prior pre-professional, college-level preparation, optometric education now requires four years, with a majority entering it possessing a baccalaureate degree. The O.D. is now universally established as the professional degree and accepted as academically equivalent to the M.D. or D.D.S.

- Six of the eleven university schools have graduate programs leading to the Ph.D. degree, providing the nucleus for basic research in vision as well as the core of education. The overwhelming majority of scientist-educators are Academy Fellows, and the main forum for reporting their research is the annual meeting of the Academy.

In Clinical Scope and Excellence

- Licensure requirements have continuously increased. All but a handful of states require candidates to take National Board Examinations.
- Forty-eight states and the District of Columbia now permit use of diagnostic pharmaceutical agents. Nineteen states permit optometric treatment of ocular disease with certain pharmaceutical agents. *
- All optometrists in the armed services are commissioned equally with those in other health professions.
- Continuing education for maintenance of practice competence is required in the vast majority of states. Continuing education programs at the national, regional, and local levels are more widespread, broader in scope, and of higher quality than ever. The Academy's Ellerbrock program has, since 1955, served as the standard of excellence for optometric continuing education.
- With few exceptions, optometrists in 1922 could pursue their profession only as private practitioners. Now there are a multitude of practice settings including Health Maintenance Organizations and other multidisciplinary clinics, hospitals, the uniformed and public health services, Veterans Administration, etc. An increasing number serve as industrial consultants and researchers.
- Optometric residencies were non-existent until 1975. Now there are more than seventy of these post-doctoral programs for the enhancement of specialized clinical expertise.

There are, in addition to those cited, other evidences of the professional and scientific advancement of optometry. Certainly the American Academy of Optometry is not solely responsible for them. But there is no doubt that its leadership and activity made the road shorter and smoother.

President Frank Brazelton, in commenting on the status of the Academy as he began his term as president, said:[21]

> It may be difficult for optometrists who have entered the profession or the Academy in recent years to appreciate how far we have come compared with those early days. Now we take for granted the independence and professional esteem which were

---

* This was the number as of May 15, 1987. At least a dozen other states had TPA laws pending at that time, and by the end of 1987, it is likely some additional states will adopt TPA laws.

so hard won. But we must not ever forget what persistent hard work and self-discipline were required to gain them and that they can be lost if we lose sight of, or neglect, the foundations of research, education, and devotion to clinical excellence on which they are based. In this respect the original goals of the Academy are as valid as ever.

Where do we go from here? Is the Academy still the trail-blazer for optometry and if so what new directions can we point out? Of the challenges to optometry over the next sixty-five years the only safe prediction is that they will be unexpected. Some signs are evident now. The scope of the profession will continue to broaden and as it does so the skirmish line with our medical brethren will continue to exist but shift to different ground. The economics of health care will remain a battle-ground where marketplace forces and social policy conflict and interact. The need and, perhaps, the demand for optometric care will increase as population demographics move the median age ever upward. The trend toward specialized clinical practice will be accentuated and lead to some form of peer certification.

The Academy is uniquely placed, because of its commitment to the education-research-practice triad to provide leadership for optometry as it faces each new challenge. One example out of many where it has done so in the past is its diplomates. It may be hard to believe that these programs, which provide the incentive and the means for self improvement in clinical expertise and its evaluation by peers, were started over 40 years ago. Another is the combination of the annual meeting program and *Journal* which provide rapid dissemination of the latest research and clinical development from the laboratory to the office.

Certainly the Academy has achieved much in its sixty-five years. But goals are generally never reached, only extended. The goals of the Academy are basically the same as when it was founded. This brief history clearly suggests that the American Academy of Optometry will continue to play a very significant role in the advancement of the profession of optometry and the enhancement of vision care for the public.

REFERENCES

1. Minutes of Executive Council. Dec 7-13, 1978, Boston, Mass.
2. Wild BW. The Academy — Preparing for the next decade. Am J Optom Physiol Opt, Nov 1979;56(11):722.
3. AAO President's Newsletter. Sept 30, 1981. AAO Archives, ILAMO; St. Louis, Mo.
4. AAO President's Newsletter. Nov 16, 1981. AOA Archives, ILAMO; St. Louis, Mo.
5. Minutes of Annual Meeting. Dec 14, 1981, Orlando, Fl.
6. Constitution and Bylaws and Guidelines for Public Statements and Information, as amended. Dec 14, 1981. AAO Archives, ILAMO; St. Louis, Mo.
7. Brazelton F. The Academy and the future: Introduction — a tradition at risk. Am J Optom Physiol Opt, Jan 1983;60(1):15-17.
8. Wolfberg MD. The Academy and competence. Ibid. 24-26.
9. Borish IM. The Academy and professionalism. Ibid. 18-23.
10. Letter to Norman Wallis, AAO Administrator, from the FTC. AAO Archives, ILAMO; St. Louis, Mo.
11. Am J Optom Physiol Opt, Oct 1986;63(10):857.
12. The documents involved and much of the correspondence relating to the FTC investigation are on file in the Washington office of the Academy.
13. Simmerman H. The Committee on Admittance. Am J Optom Arch Am Acad Optom, Oct 1966;37(10):939-940.
14. Flom MC. President's 1981 report to the American Academy of Optometry. Am J Optom Physiol Opt, Apr 1983;60(4):269-272.
15. Ibid. 273-277.
16. Minutes of Executive Council, Dec 5-11, 1984. St. Louis, Mo.
17. Minutes of Executive Council, June 16, 1979. Owatonna, Minn.
18. Minutes of Executive Council, Apr 4-5, 1981. New Orleans, La.
19. Heath GG. Report of President, Dec 10, 1984. Am J Optom Physiol Opt, May 1984:61(5):347-349.
20. Wolfberg MD. Report of the President to the American Academy of Optometry. Am J Optom Physiol Opt, May 1986;66(5):311-312.
21. Based upon material furnished the author by Brazelton during preparation of the manuscript.

APPENDIX

CHRONOLOGY

AMERICAN ACADEMY OF OPTOMETRY

January 1922. Nine optometrists and two medical doctors met in St. Louis and began formation of an organization for "optometric study in higher branches and for exchange of ideas in optometric work." Morris Steinfeld was elected director.

June 1922. A permanent organization, the American Academy of Optometry, was formed, with Morris Steinfeld as the first chairman. The stated goals were to raise the standards of optometric practice, education, and ethics.

December 1922. First annual meeting held with presentation of papers, luncheons and dinners, business sessions, and election of officers.

June 1924. Adoption of the Constitution and Bylaws by the membership at the Third Annual Meeting, which included standards of practice required for membership.

December 1925. Beginning of publication of the *Transactions of the American Academy of Optometry*, which carried the scientific papers presented at the annual meetings. These continued for thirteen volumes ending in 1939.

May 1928. The *American Journal of Optometry* became the official news organ of the American Academy of Optometry, though it did not publish papers presented at the annual meetings.

January 1929. American Academy of Optometry incorporated in Washington, D.C.

November 1929. First local chapters granted charters: Maryland, November 5, and Minnesota, November 6.

December 1929. Membership passed the 100 mark, and attendance at the annual meeting was becoming large enough to attract attention of scientists as a place to present results of research.

November 1930. First research fellowship established at Columbia University, awarded to William Feinbloom.

December 1936. A public relations committee appointed to supply the press with information about subjects presented at the annual meetings.

June 1938. Establishment of an editorial committee to review and select papers to be presented at the annual meetings.

December 1940. Examinations for membership in the Academy given to more than sixty applicants during the annual meeting. This was the first time an achievement test was required, and an instruction manual had been prepared for guidance for applications.

The suggestion was made that in addition to submitting cases and passing an examination for initial membership, a recertification examination be required periodically for all members.

January 1941. Beginning of publication of the *American Journal of Optometry and Archives of the American Academy of Optometry,* which became the official source for publication of the papers presented at the Academy meetings and its business transactions, as well as news items.

May 1942. Decision to sponsor publication of the first book, *Hering's Special Sense and Movement of the Eye.*

December 1944. Adoption of a plan to establish special sections on contact lenses and orthoptics.

December 1945. Academy was recovering from reduction in activity during the war years. Membership was about 350 with a number of non-optometric scientists on the rolls. A larger number and a higher quality of papers were being presented at the annual meetings.

Beginning of recognition and awards program. Honorary Life Fellowship awarded to Alpheus Smith, Ohio State University.

May 1946. Sections on pathology and aniseikonia were established and chairmen appointed.

December 1947. The Contact Lens Section adopted a plan to certify diplomates in contact lenses.

December 1950. Membership exceeded 500, and more than 200 attended the annual meetings, with papers being presented by many researchers and extensive programs of clinical discussion held during the various section meetings.

December 1952. First individual who was primarily an educator, Meredith W. Morgan, became president of the Academy. This marked the beginning of a balance of educators and practitioners on the Executive Council and the establishment of the Academy as no longer primarily an organization of optometrists seeking more education but as a forum for communication between visual scientists as well.

December 1953. A committee appointed to study a proposal to offer post-graduate courses on a variety of topics just prior to the annual meeting.

December 1954. First meeting held outside the United States, the Thirty-Third Annual Meeting, convened at the Royal York Hotel, Toronto, Ontario, Canada.

December 1955. Postgraduate courses first presented in Chicago, with forty-one instructors presenting forty different courses totaling 104 hours of instruction.

July 1957. Publication of the *Sheard Volume,* a collection of papers written by Charles Sheard, made possible by the subscription of funds from several sources.

October 1959. Beginning of publication of the American Academy of Optometry Series, home study courses on various topics. Volume 1 was *Synopsis of Glaucoma,* by Arthur Shlaifer.

December 1962. Academy members, following the annual meeting, attend an interprofessional forum held in Bogata, Columbia. There were now AAO members in about fifteen countries outside the United States.

December 1963. Presentation of the first Prentice Medal to W.A.H. Rushton. The award had been established in 1958 but was not awarded until this date.

Beginning of the Science Information Program to supply information about visual science to the public press, which continued for five years.

January 1967. Extension of the diplomate program to the field of orthoptics and vision training.

June 1968. Size and activity of the Academy reached a point where reorganization of its operation became essential to continue to achieve its goals. Plans made to accomplish this.

October 1971. Programs were planned for the Fiftieth Annual Meeting by each of the now seven sections — Binocular Vision and Perception, Communication and Information, Contact Lenses, Optometric Education, Pathology, Public Health and Occupational Optometry, and Refraction, the latter with sub-sections on aniseikonia and low vision.

December 1971. Diplomate program in the Section on Binocular Vision and Perception approved. First candidates examined and certified in December 1972.

December 1972. Presented at the annual meeting were 122 postgraduate courses, 123 papers in the general program, 162 presentations in the section meetings, and two invited papers, totaling 409.

Diplomate program in low vision approved, including the provision that certification would be good for only five years with a recertification process then required. First diplomates certified in December 1973.

November 1973. The end of an era for the Academy with the death of Carel C. Koch, who had been its secretary for thirty-three years and editor of the *Journal* for forty-four years.

December 1973. The Academy purchased the *American Journal of Optometry* and changed the name of the publication to the *American Journal of Optometry and Physiological Optics.* John Schoen was appointed secretary to replace Carel C. Koch.

December 1974. A period of transition, with activity in reorganization of the administrative structure and the secretary's office of the Academy and establishing a publisher for the *Journal.* Much of this continued for the next few years.

December 1976. Special committee appointed to review entire admissions procedure and membership standards. This was the beginning of concern about the standards and their relationship to changing attitudes about regulation of ethics and professionalism.

April 1977. The Academy went abroad, meeting in London with the British Chapter as host.

December 1977. Ad Hoc Committee on Admissions made a number of recommendations. Many were adopted and became the basis for revisions in the admissions procedures to the form in use today.

March 1978. Publication of a *Manual On Policies,* which codified the policies of the Academy and outlined its administrative and business procedures. This, along with formalization of its operation, aided greatly in preparing the way for employment of a professional management company.

December 1978. Because of concern about the U.S. Federal Trade Commission ruling against prohibition of advertising, the Executive Council voted to set aside the provision in its bylaws prohibiting advertising. This was later determined to be invalid because it was not voted upon by the members.

June 1979. Beginning of study and development of a plan to completely reorganize the Academy's operation and to move the office to an appropriate city location.

December 1981. Bylaws revised in regard to membership standards in an attempt to conform to legal requirements. This was an historic point because it represented what, at least in the minds of some, amounted to lowering some of the traditional standards of conduct which had been the foundation of the Academy from its very beginning.

June 1982. Academy office moved to Washington, D.C., with Norman Wallis as first administrator.

July 1982. Academy received notice from the FTC that its membership requirements would be reviewed. This led to further minor amendments in the bylaws and guidelines to members, which were approved by the membership in December 1985. A consent decree relating to this matter was released by the FTC in October 1986.

December 1984. To clarify an issue of concern because of the growing attention to credentialing and certification, the Executive Council expressed the position that neither Academy fellowship nor section diplomate status constitute certification of specialization, and that diplomates are knowledge based, not competency based.

September 1985. With administrative transition, reorganization, and legal and ethical problems resolved to some degree, the Executive Council held a long-range planning meeting and outlined a number of major subjects to be addressed for the future.

December 1986. Academy membership in all categories totaled 3,274, with members in some twenty-eight countries. Attendance at its annual meeting was close to 1,300.

HISTORY OF THE JOURNAL

AMERICAN ACADEMY OF OPTOMETRY

In January, 1924, the first issue of a new optometric journal appeared. The *Northwest Journal of Optometry* was published in Minneapolis, Minnesota, by the Minnesota, North Dakota, and South Dakota optometric associations. In September 1924, Nebraska joined the sponsoring state associations. The new journal printed scientific articles, book reviews, abstracts of current literature in allied journals, and editorial comment on the emerging optometric associations. The founder of the *Journal* and its first editor was Carel C. Koch, a twenty-eight-year-old Minneapolis optometrist.

After nineteen issues of the *Northwest Journal of Optometry* had appeared, the name was changed to the *American Journal of Optometry,* the new name being used first on Volume 2, Number 8. The content, editorial staff, and purpose remained the same, and by that time, the Iowa and Oklahoma optometric associations had joined the group of sponsoring associations using the *Journal* as an official organ. By 1928, when Volume 5 appeared, the number of state associations using the *American Journal of Optometry* as their official journal had increased to eleven. With Volume 5, May 1928, the *Journal* became an official news organ of the American Academy of Optometry and it so continued from 1928 until 1940. *

The Academy, however, published separately the scientific papers read at each of its annual meetings; included were the Transactions of the Executive Council and Annual Meetings. Thirteen bound volumes were published incorporating the papers read at the fourth through the eighteenth annual meetings (two volumes each contain the proceedings of two meetings). These bound volumes were printed for the Academy as *Transactions of the American Academy of Optometry* by the American Journal of Optometry Publishing Association. The thirteenth volume, the *Transactions of the Eighteenth Annual Meeting,* was published in 1939. In 1940, a committee of the American Academy of Optometry studied the matter of publications and decided to merge the Academy publications with the *American Journal of Optometry.*

---

* The *American Journal of Optometry* continued to serve as the official publication of various state associations until January 1934. From that time on there was no listing in the *Journal* of state associations using it as an official publication. Thus, if there is any specific date for the beginning of the *Journal* as primarily a scientific publication, it would be January 1934.

The new publication appeared as the *American Journal of Optometry and Archives of the American Academy of Optometry*. The volume was exactly what the name implied — two different publications: the *Journal,* privately owned (primarily by Koch), and the *Archives,* owned by the Academy. Under the terms of the agreement, the American Journal of Optometry Publishing Company was responsible for the *Journal,* and agreed to publish all papers read at the annual meeting. The Academy paid the *Journal* subscriptions for all Academy Fellows. The *Journal* had several thousand subscribers. The *Journal* also carried many news items pertaining to the Academy.

The publication of the *Journal and Archives* was highly successful, and during the period of the joint publication, it became a leading journal for the presentation of new and original papers on both basic visual science and clinical optometry. It also carried Academy news and reports of its business affairs.

The *Journal* was edited by Carel C. Koch for forty-four years. J.I. Kurtz was first business manager and then associate editor. He remained with the *Journal* until 1939. During the early days the two optometrists, among the first to practice in professional offices in Minnesota, did most of the journal work themselves. Kurtz, when practice was slow in the early days, stuffed magazines into envelopes and prepared the mailings. Koch did a great deal of the writing himself and all of the technical editing unassisted. The first volume of the *Journal* listed six optometrists as associate editors: E.O. Fjelstad, Red Wing, Minnesota; A.H. Nordland, Minneapolis, Minnesota; H.B. Kollofski, St. Paul, Minnesota; A.R. Burquist, Duluth, Minnesota; A.S. Anderson, Fessenden, North Dakota; and A.M. Skeffington, Kearny, Nebraska.

Although there were several associate editors, a great amount of the writing in the early volumes of the *Journal* — articles, reviews, papers, editorials, and abstracts — was done by Carel Koch; a lesser but substantial number of articles were written by his colleague and associate, J.I. Kurtz.

By the time Volume 2 appeared, the number of associate editors was reduced to only Kurtz and Fjelstad. A group of state editors for reporting various state proceedings was retained. In Volume 2, the state editor from Nebraska, A.M. Skeffington, was replaced by E.B. Alexander who later, with Skeffington, formed the Optometric Extension Program. By the time Volume 4 appeared, the number of associate editors was reduced to J.I. Kurtz.

The *American Journal of Optometry,* in addition to associate editors from time to time, also listed on its masthead for several years an editorial board, consisting of two or three people who presumably provided some policy-making advice. Also listed were collaborators, as many as seventy or eighty at a time. Presumably they were individuals who were potential authors of papers for the *Journal.*

The first issue of the *American Journal of Optometry and the Archives of the American Academy of Optometry,* January 1941, carried on its masthead the names of Carel Koch, Guy L. DuPlessis, and Clarence W. Morris as editors, though no doubt Koch was editor and the other two associate editors. In addition there was listed an editorial council of eight people and twelve associate editor referees. Thus a refereeing system was being used, and in fact may have been used to a less formal degree prior to that time. By January 1953, the masthead listed only Koch as editor and an editorial council of seventeen people. That is basically the same format that has been used since, with the addition of associate and assistant editors when appropriate, and occasionally other editorial staff assistance.

Carel Koch was both editor and publisher of the *Journal* from its beginning until 1968, assisted in various ways by others as described above. Monroe J. Hirsch followed Koch as editor. He had been associate editor since 1953. Grace Weiner, who replaced Hirsch as associate editor, had joined the staff as bibliographic editor in 1958. Weiner was associate editor until 1976.

The *Journal* operated much along the same basic policy and philosophy during the years Koch served as the publisher, with Koch the dominant individual in the editor's role. After Hirsch became editor, Koch was still publisher, and he exerted considerable influence upon the *Journal*. Use of an editorial council was continued and the system of refereeing papers by experts was formalized and expanded. A great many individuals have served on the editorial council over the years. It consisted of from six or eight to as many as thirty. The number functioning as referees of papers submitted to the journal ran as high as 300 in 1986.

There was concern however among Academy leaders about what would happen upon the death of Carel Koch, who was the principal owner of the publishing company. Some tentative plans were made for a transition, but little was actually done. When a change of publishers became necessary at the end of 1973, a number of problems arose, since the *Journal* had been dominated for so long by a small group.

The American Journal of Optometry Publishing Company was a partnership with seven equal shares. Carel Koch owned three shares and Mrs. Koch owned two shares, while Monroe J. Hirsch and John Schoen, who served as editor and business manager, respectively, each owned one share. The partnership agreement stated that upon the death of any partner, the remaining partners had first option to purchase the shares of the deceased partner. Schoen and Hirsch had assured the Executive Council that in the event of the death of Koch, they would purchase the remaining shares and would then sell the entire *Journal* to the Academy with no profit to themselves. The Executive Council, beginning with the presidency of J. Donald Kratz in 1965, set up a fund to be used in the ultimate purchase of the *Journal*.

In 1973, when Carel and Mrs. Koch died within a few weeks of each other, the ownership of the *Journal* changed hands. Hirsch and Schoen exercised their options and purchased the Koch shares, and immediately sold the entire *Journal* to the Academy for exactly what they had paid for it. The *Journal* was renamed the *American Journal of Optometry and Physiological Optics*, an appropriate title since physiological optics and clinical optometry were the principal topic areas.

For almost fifty years, Carel C. Koch had been the publisher of the *Journal*. Upon his death, and with the Academy assuming ownership, it became necessary to obtain a new publisher. A proposal was made to the Academy by the Professional Press, Inc., which already published *The Optometric Weekly*, suggesting that it would supply the *Weekly* to its subscribers for forty weeks of the year and the *Journal* for the remaining twelve weeks. Thus, during the period that the Professional Press served as publisher, the *Journal* was received by the 2,000 Academy Fellows, also by more than 10,000 optometrists who were non-Academy members and subscribers to the *Weekly*. The Professional Press served as publisher of the *Journal* in 1974 and 1975. During this time the Academy was still solely responsible for the editorial content of the *Journal*, with the Professional Press being responsible for printing, advertising, and distribution.

In the summer of 1975, it was mutually agreed by the Professional Press and the Academy to end their relationship. Since January 1976, the *Journal* has been published by the Williams & Wilkins Company, which publishes a number of scientific journals. The *Journal* is still owned by the Academy, and the Academy is responsible for its contents. Williams and Wilkins Company prints the publication and handles advertising and business details.

Monroe Hirsch edited the *Journal* until July 1976. At that time Merton Flom began to function as editor on an interim basis. Flom was on the Executive Council and on the faculty at the School of Optometry, University of Houston. Those responsibilities, plus the fact that there was some uncertainty as to whether or not Hirsch would return as editor, were the reasons Flom functioned only as an interim editor. An Ad Hoc Committee was appointed to recommend a new editor in 1978. William M. Lyle, a professor of optometry at the University of Waterloo, was selected and began as editor in January 1979. Lyle has been the editor ever since. In 1981, T. David Williams became an associate editor and Walter W. Chase was added as assistant editor in 1985.

The first volume of the *Journal* in 1924 contained only 280 pages, including advertising; the annual subscription rate was three dollars. This was reduced to two dollars the following year and remained at this level until Volume 5 when it was raised back to three dollars. Volume 5 in 1928 contained 638 pages including advertising; thus the content had doubled in the first half-decade. *

---

* Beginning in January 1920 a quarterly journal called the *American Journal of Physiological Optics* began publication with Charles Sheard as editor. This journal was published by the Research Division of the American Optical Company. Seven volumes of four issues each were published, the last in October 1926. The first issue contained a photograph and an article about Thomas Young, who was called the "father of psychological optics." The journal carried a wide range of topics and editorials, most of which were written by various scientists, some medical doctors, and a few optometrists. Most of the authors were not at that time appearing on Academy

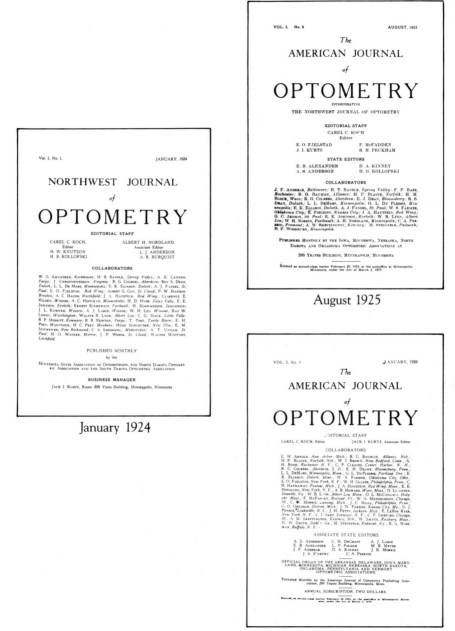

January 1924

August 1925

January 1928

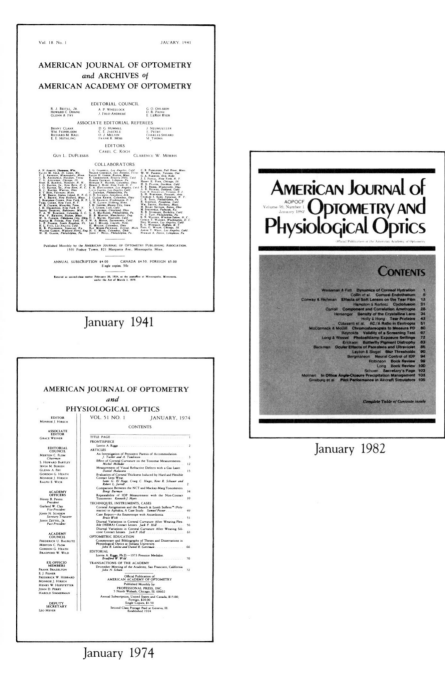

January 1941

January 1974

January 1982

By 1940, the seventeenth volume, and the last before the *Journal* merged with
the *Academy Archives*, contained 584 pages exclusive of advertising; the
annual subscription rate was four dollars. The first issue after affiliation with
the Academy was essentially the same size and cost. During the next quarter-
century, however, due to monetary inflation, the subscription rate increased.
Volume 44 in 1967 was ten dollars; this was increased to twelve dollars in 1968
for Volume 45, and reached fifty-five dollars in 1986. The size of the *Journal* also
increased markedly as the optometric profession matured and more and more
research was reported in its pages. By the 1960s the *Journal* was running well
over 800 pages, exclusive of advertising, in each volume. In 1986 the total was
1,016 pages.

In 1941, when the *Journal* became the monthly organ of the Academy,
adopting the new name, *American Journal of Optometry and Archives of the
American Academy of Optometry*, the editor stated:

> The new name embodies the old as well as the new, and we hope
> that the journals to come will also embody all that is good of the old
> *Journal* as well as the best of the Academy, as it has functioned, and as
> it is functioning today. The editorial policies remain the same as they
> have since this publication was started in 1924. This primarily is a
> technical publication and will continue to remain one.

The *Journal* has served three basic functions over the years, much as the
editor had projected in 1941:

1. A journal of clinical optometry. This was the heritage of the first
Northwest Journal of Optometry. From the first issue to the present, the *Journal*
has encouraged the publication of clinical optometric material presented in a
scientific manner.

2. A journal of physiological optics. This was also envisioned in the founda-
tion of the *Journal* and was a role further adopted with the demise of the
American Journal of Physiological Optics and with the incorporation of the
Academy Archives into the *Journal*.

3. A journal reporting the official transactions of the American Academy of
Optometry. After the merging of the two publications in 1941, the *Journal* spoke
editorially for the Academy.

In recent years there has been less editorial matter and news items. Direct
communication with members, beginning in 1981, has been carried on by
publication of a president's newsletter. Thus the third purpose of the *Journal* is
less important today.

---

programs or publishing in the *American Journal of Optometry*. When the *American
Journal of Physiological Optics* ceased publication, these authors had to look elsewhere
for a journal in which to publish. Many undoubtedly turned to the *American Journal of
Optometry* and this was a factor in its rapid growth in size.

However, the first two — functioning as a journal for physiological optics and for clinical optometry — are still its primary purpose. History certainly demonstrates that it is very effectively accomplishing that goal. The pages of this journal over the years clearly detail the scientific development of the profession of optometry.

FORMATION AND ACTIVITY
OF THE CHAPTERS
AMERICAN ACADEMY OF OPTOMETRY

The first chapter of this history of the Academy discusses briefly some of the early academies of optometry, a few being the forerunners of some that still exist. Those organizations were formed independently, however, and were not affiliated with the American Academy of Optometry, at least in the beginning.

The American Academy itself began to organize local chapters in 1929. The idea was that all members of the local chapters were to be members of the Academy and that a chapter would be granted a charter and required to follow guidelines set down by the parent body. Advantages were that a local group could meet frequently and offer an opportunity for more exchange of information, etc.

The idea was sound and in some cases worked quite well. Success in a local area was highly dependent upon the enthusiasm and capability of the individuals involved and relatively little upon any leadership and motivation from the AAO. Some chapters thrived, with excellent programs and social events that attracted and held members. But interest generally varied from time to time, and many chapters ceased functioning.

It is difficult to put together a detailed and accurate history of the chapters of the Academy. Communication was meager at times and records equally so. The attention the parent body gave to its affiliates depended upon other priorities and the availability of some member with interest in developing chapter activity. In recent years more attention has been given to the chapters and attempts made to generate interest. Efforts were also made to determine which ones are active and indeed whether each is a legally qualified chapter.

Here is a summary of the chapters that have been chartered over the years and the status of each as of October 1986. There may well be some groups using the term Chapter of the American Academy of Optometry but not actually recognized by the parent body. Some may have been affiliated, failed to pay dues, and dropped from the official roster.

CHARTERS GRANTED TO CHAPTERS

No.	Date	Status	Name of Local Academy
1	Nov. 5, 1929	revoked	Maryland
2	Nov. 6, 1929	revoked	Minnesota
3	Jan. 10, 1930	active	New York Academy of Optometry
4	Jan. 22, 1930	active	Michigan
5	Feb. 8, 1930	active	Nebraska
6	Feb. 21, 1930	active	Indiana
7	Mar. 27, 1930	revoked	Arkansas
8	Probably 1933	active	New Jersey
9	Sept. 17, 1943	active	Paducah, Kentucky
10	date unknown	active	Cuyahoga Academy of Optometry— now Northeast Ohio
11	date unknown	revoked	Iowa
12	June 1, 1946	merged	Vermont and New Hampshire— now New England
13	Jan. 1, 1947	active	Eastern Pennsylvania
14	Jan. 15, 1947	revoked	Central Ohio
15	Nov. 1, 1947	revoked	Illinois
16	Nov. 1, 1947	revoked	North Carolino
17	July 1, 1949	revoked	Northwest Pacific
18	Dec. 14, 1950	revoked	Upstate New York
19	Dec. 14, 1950	active	San Francisco Bay Area— now California
20	Dec. 14, 1950	active	British
21	Dec. 8, 1951	revoked	Delaware
22	May 21, 1952	inactive	Texas
23	July 1, 1954	revoked	Cincinnati
24	Dec. 11, 1954	revoked	Georgia
25	Dec. 11, 1955	inactive	Dayton, Ohio
26	Feb. 21, 1957	revoked	Alberta
27	Dec. 1958		unknown
28	Dec. 1958	active	San Gabriel Valley, California
29	Dec. 1958	active	New England
30	Dec. 7, 1959	inactive	Iowa
31	Dec. 7, 1959	active	Western Pennsylvania
32	Dec. 7, 1959	revoked	Colorado
33	Nov. 20, 1961	inactive	Hawaii
34	Dec. 13, 1965	inactive	Virginia
35	date unknown	revoked	Kentucky
36	Dec. 13, 1965	revoked	South Africa
37	Nov. 1974	inactive	Nebraska
38	Dec. 1973	revoked	Kentucky
39	1973	inactive	Puerto Rico
42	Dec. 16, 1974*	active	Missouri
43	Dec. 12, 1979	active	Quebec
44	date unknown	active	Orange County, California
45	Jan. 10, 1982	active	Oklahoma
46	Dec. 1984	inactive	Utah
47	Dec. 1984	inactive	Western New York—So. Ontario

* There is no record of numbers 40 and 41.

ORIGIN AND DEVELOPMENT
OF THE SECTIONS

AMERICAN ACADEMY OF OPTOMETRY

The history of the sections is difficult to determine accurately. There is no continuing record of their origin and development and certainly little indication of the individuals who were the instigators or founders. The minutes do not show with accuracy the exact date of approval by the Executive Council to form a section. Approval was solely by the Council and never by a vote of the membership. In several instances a chairman of a section was appointed or a section program appeared at the annual meeting without any prior documentation as to the origin of the section, at least none that was available. In addition, the exact name of the sections and changes in their names are not clearly recorded.

However, a reasonably accurate outline of the origin and development of the sections is possible. At least the sequence and approximate time frame are appropriate.* The establishment of sections of the Academy began in 1944. There had been some discussion about the need for a vehicle for optometrists with interest in so-called specialty areas to meet together prior to that time, but no action was taken. The records available do not show the names of the individuals involved nor who was appointed to carry out the actual establishment of the sections. But in December 1944 the Executive Council adopted a proposal to incorporate special sections, with contact lenses and orthoptics being suggested. Thus these two were the first, and both began functioning in 1945.

The Contact Lens Section was the first to institute a program of certification. The individuals who passed the examination were granted diplomate status. Approval to proceed with the diplomate program was given in December 1947, and the first diplomates were certified a year later.** The name was changed to the Section on Cornea and Contact Lenses in 1982.

The Section on Orthoptics, now called Binocular Vision and Perception, though it began its activities in 1945, did not institute its diplomate program

---

* Chapter 6 includes a brief description of the sections as they existed in 1961. This provides a sense of their scope, purpose, and function at that time. The operational basis of the sections is still much the same.
** Chapter 4 contains a description of the credentialing process at that time, which is typical of the system in use by the various diplomate programs at present.

until 1971 when approved by the Executive Council. The first diplomates were certified in 1972. In recent years the names of the diplomates in the various sections have been listed in the annual membership directory.

The Section on Aniseikonia began functioning in 1949. This was the era of considerable interest in this topic and it certainly was considered a specialty. Since it actually dealt with refraction, that term was soon added to the section name and it became the section on Refraction and Aniseikonia. There was some consideration given to a diplomate program in aniseikonia, but interest in the subject soon waned and the term itself disappeared. The name of the section was changed to Refractive Problems in 1967. This section became the Section on Primary Care in 1977.

The Section on Occupational Vision was established in 1951. A section meeting was held the following year and papers were presented. The section has continued since then with some change of emphasis. The term Public Health was added in 1960, and it is now known as the Section on Public Health and Occupational Vision. A diplomate program in Public Health was instituted in 1986, and two honorary diplomate awards were made.

In 1967 a Section on Communications and Information was created. It was to deal with information retrieval, computers, and audiovisual techniques, which it did for several years, but it ceased to function in 1973.

The Section on Pathology began functioning in 1949. It has held sessions at the annual meetings ever since. The name was changed to the Section on Disease in 1977.

A Section on Optometric Education was instituted in 1971. Membership was limited to educators, and the section was designed to provide a forum for exchange of ideas. Programs have been held at the annual meetings ever since then.

The Section on Visual Science was authorized in 1971 and held its first meeting at the 1972 annual meeting. It continues to function in the same general format as it has from its beginning.

Low vision was originally a topic included in the Contact Lens Section. It then became a subsection of that section and later a subsection in the Section on Refraction. In 1972 a prospectus was submitted for a diplomate program, and it was approved. The first examinations were given in December 1973. In 1977 it was approved as a separate section and has had its own program since then. The low-vision diplomate program is unique in that certification is good for only five years. Thus it is the first program to require a recertification of competency after original diplomate status.

POSTGRADUATE EDUCATION PROGRAM

AMERICAN ACADEMY OF OPTOMETRY

The beginnings of postgraduate education by the Academy are described in Chapter 5 and its development discussed in other places throughout this book. This is but a brief summary to highlight a few significant points.

In December 1950, the Executive Council adopted a recommendation that short courses in aniseikonia, orthoptics, and contact lenses be offered in cooperation with schools of optometry in the convention city prior to the annual meeting. It is not clear whether the Academy or the school would actually offer the courses, but it matters little since it was never done. The subject received little or no attention until three years later when a committee was appointed to study a proposal to present a five-day program of clinical and graduate courses prior to or following the annual meeting. Appointed chairman was Vincent J. Ellerbrock, who apparently was one of the chief proponents of the plan, with members J. Donald Kratz, Charles Stewart, and Carel C. Koch.

The committee recommended in December 1954 that such courses be instigated, and outlined what they might be and how presented. The first program was offered in Chicago in December 1955 in the three days preceding the annual meeting. Forty courses were presented by forty-one instructors. That amazing total for the initial effort indicated the great interest in and need for postgraduate education that existed, and at the same time it was a testimony to the hard and diligent work of the committee in arranging such an extensive choice of topics. Courses varied in length from one hour to fourteen hours, with a total of 116 hours of education available.

The original success was by no means a temporary phenomenon. The postgraduate courses grew steadily in number and in attendance from that first time. Much was due to the skill and labor of Vincent Ellerbrock who was chairman for the first ten years. He died suddenly just before the 1965 program. The name was then changed to the Ellerbrock Postgraduate Education Program.

The program has varied little in its purpose, design, or format since its beginning. Fees for attendance were on a per-course basis until 1985 when a single registration fee plan was adopted, making administration considerably less complicated. Honoraria for instructors has been changed somewhat, and certainly the use of audiovisuals has expanded tremendously. The course selection process has been refined and the quality of the courses greatly improved, and they have been accepted for continuing education credits by most state boards requiring them. Course subjects have kept pace with the changing needs of the profession, and the variety of the subjects increased as well.

Chairmen of the Continuing Education Committee have been:

1955–1964	Vincent J. Ellerbrock
1965–1971	Bradford W. Wild
1972–1976	Frank Brazelton
1977–1984	Jess B. Eskridge
1985–1986	David W. Hansen

Great credit goes to them and the many committee members for development and maintenance of an excellent postgraduate education program. For comparison to the 1955 program shown here, the 1986 program in Toronto, Canada, offered 110 courses covering 188 hours of instruction, and fourteen workshops of thirty-five instructional hours, with 101 individual lecturers.

POSTGRADUATE COURSES
THIRTY-FOURTH ANNUAL MEETING
AMERICAN ACADEMY OF OPTOMETRY, CHICAGO
DECEMBER 1955

1. Morton L. Abrams, LL.B., D.O.S. Legal Aspects of Optometry
2. Merrill J. Allen, O.D., Ph.D. Raubitscheck Arrow Test for Astigmatism
3. Neil J. Bailey, O.D., Ph.D. Amblyopia, Suppression and Related Phenomena
4. Robert E. Bannon, O.D. Problems of Anisometropia
5. Robert G. Bannon, O.D. Prebyopic Additions — Physiological Basis
6. Robert G. Bannon, O.D. Oblique Astigmatism
7. Edwin W. Bechtold, O.D. Design of Eikonic Lenses
8. Lois B. Bing, O.D. Visual Screening of School Children
9. C.S. Bridgman, O.D., Ph.D. Visual Efficiency and Industrial Performance
10. Jack C. Copeland, O.D. Streak Retinoscopy
11. Margaret S. Dowaliby, O.D. Design in Eyewear
12. Jack Neill, O.D., William Feinbloom, O.D., Ph.D., William Policoff, O.D. The Design and Fitting of Contact Lenses
13. Isidore S. Feinbloom, O.D., Ph.D. Visual Rehabilitation of the Partially Blind
14. Bernard Rossett, O.D. Optics of Contact Lenses
15. Glenn A. Fry, O.D., Ph.D. Physiological Basis of Discomfort from Glare
16. Glenn A. Fry, O.D., Ph.D. Analysis of Problems with Retinoscopy
17. Robert Graham, O.D. Non-glass Ophthalmic Lenses
18. Robert Graham, O.D. Contact Lenses Currently in Use
19. Salvi S. Grupposo, O.D. The Stereoscope as an Orthoptic Instrument
20. Sylvester K. Guth, E.E., D.O.S. Recommended Lighting Levels and Their Measurements
21. Gordon G. Heath, O.D. Office Diagnosis of Color Defects

22. Monroe J. Hirsch, O.D., Ph.D.   The Elements of Statistical Reasoning
23. Charles Abel, O.D., Merrill Allen, O.D., Ph.D., H.W. Hofstetter, O.D., Ph.D.   Graphic Analysis of Optometric Findings
24. Isidore Kaplan, M.D.   Pharmacology Pertaining to the Eye
25. Alfred Lit, Ph.D.   Dark and Light Adaptation
26. Bernard Mazow, O.D.   An Introduction to Slit Lamp Microscopy
27. David D. Michaels, O.D.   Physical and Differential Diagnosis in Optometry
28. T.R. Murroughs, O.D.   Strabismus Testing and Diagnosis
29. J. Neumueller, O.D.   Distortion of Steroscopic Spatial Localization
30. J. Neumueller, O.D.   Introduction to Aniseikonia
31. Henry B. Peters, O.D.   Turville Infinity Balance Test
32. William W. Policoff, O.D.   Aids for the Partially Blind
33. Herman Sager, O.D.   Pitfalls in Industrial Vision and Design of Occupational Eyewear
34. Carl F. Shepard, O.D.   Visual Acuity Charts
35. Harold Simmerman, O.D.   Scleral and Corneal Tonometry
36. Ralph C. Wick, O.D., Monroe J. Hirsch, O.D., Ph.D.   Glaucoma
37. Harold Simmerman, O.D., Frederic W. Sinn, O.D.   Management of the Cataract Patient
38. Newton K. Wesley, O.D.   The Fitting of the Microlens
39. Ralph E. Wick, O.D.   Geriatrics and Optometry
40. Daniel Woolf, O.D., Ph.D.   Fixation Disparity as a Diagnostic Method

PRESIDENTS AND ANNUAL MEETING DATES

AMERICAN ACADEMY OF OPTOMETRY

Elected at the Meeting	Date of Annual Meeting	Location of Meeting
The first meeting was organizational in nature, called by Morris Steinfeld.	Jan. 11, 1922	Planters Hotel, St. Louis, Mo.
Steinfeld was elected temporary chairman at the second meeting. *	June 2, 1922	Claypoole Hotel, Indianapolis, Ind.
Morris Steinfeld, Paducah, Ky. 1st Chairman	Dec. 9–13, 1922 1st Annual Meeting	American Annex Hotel, St. Louis, Mo.
Eugene G. Wiseman Buffalo, N.Y. 2d Chairman	Dec. 10–11, 1923 2d Annual Meeting	Rochester, N.Y.
Eugene G. Wiseman	June 9–11, 1924 3d Annual Meeting	Kansas City, Mo.
Eugene G. Wiseman	Dec. 13–14, 1925 4th Annual Meeting	Hotel Touraine, Buffalo, N.Y.
Eugene G. Wiseman	Dec. 5–7, 1926 5th Annual Meeting	Hotel Raleigh, Washington, D.C.
Eugene G. Wiseman	Dec. 4–6, 1927 6th Annual Meeting	Hotel Pennsylvania, New York, N.Y.
Carel C. Koch Minneapolis, Minn. 3d Chairman	Dec. 2–4, 1928 7th Annual Meeting	Morrison Hotel, Chicago, Ill.
Briggs S. Palmer Boston, Mass. 4th Chairman	Dec. 15–18, 1929 8th Annual Meeting	Statler Hotel, Boston, Mass.
Walter I. Brown New Bedford, Mass. 5th Chairman	Dec. 14–16, 1930 9th Annual Meeting	Hotel Fontenelle, Omaha, Nebr.

* This meeting was also organizational. No papers were read and there were no official functions, thus it is not counted as an annual meeting.

Walter I. Brown	Dec. 6–8, 1931 10th Annual Meeting	Benjamin Franklin Hotel, Philadelphia, Pa.
O.J. Melvin Omaha, Nebr. 6th Chairman	Dec. 18–20, 1932 11th Annual Meeting	Palmer House Hotel, Chicago, Ill.
O.J. Melvin	Dec. 17–19, 1933 12th Annual Meeting	Lord Baltimore Hotel, Baltimore, Md.
Robert N. Walker Winston-Salem, N.C. 7th Chairman	Dec. 16–18, 1934 13th Annual Meeting	Statler Hotel, Cleveland, Ohio
Robert N. Walker	Dec. 25–27, 1935 14th Annual Meeting	Governor Clinton Hotel, New York, N.Y.
Richard M. Hall Cleveland, Ohio 8th Chairman	Aug. 23–25, 1936 15th Annual Meeting	Blackstone Hotel, Chicago, Ill.
Richard M. Hall	June 24–26, 1937 16th Annual Meeting	Seneca Hotel, Rochester, N.Y.
Don R. Paine Topeka, Kans. 9th Chairman	June 22–24, 1938 17th Annual Meeting	John Marshall Hotel, Richmond, Va.
Don R. Paine	June 22–24, 1939 18th Annual Meeting	Biltmore Hotel, Los Angeles, Calif.
Arthur P. Wheelock Des Moines, Iowa 10th President*	Dec. 8–10, 1940 19th Annual Meeting	Morrison Hotel, Chicago, Ill.
Arthur P. Wheelock	Dec. 7–9, 1941 20th Annual Meeting	Morrison Hotel, Chicago, Ill.
Arthur P. Wheelock	May 16, 1942 21st Annual Meeting**	Morrison Hotel, Chicago, Ill.
Arthur P. Wheelock	July 15, 1943 22nd Annual Meeting	Hotel Cleveland, Cleveland, Ohio
J. Fred Andreae Baltimore, Md. 11th President	Dec. 10–12, 1944 23d Annual Meeting	Stevens Hotel, Chicago, Ill.
J. Fred Andreae	Dec. 9–12, 1945 24th Annual Meeting	Deshler Wallick Hotel, Columbus, Ohio
Harold M. Fisher New York, N.Y. 12th President	May 18–21, 1947 25th Annual Meeting	Bellevue Stratford Hotel, Philadelphia, Pa.
Harold M. Fisher	Dec. 13–16, 1947 26th Annual Meeting	Palmer House Hotel, Chicago, Ill.

* In 1940 the title was changed from Chairman to President.
** In 1942 and 1943, because of the war, there was no membership meeting with presentation of papers; however, the Executive Council met officially and members could attend, thus the meetings were designated as annual meetings.

Daniel G. Hummel New York, N.Y. 13th President	Dec. 4–7, 1948 27th Annual Meeting	Robert E. Lee Hotel, Winston-Salem, N.C.
Daniel G. Hummel	Dec. 10–13, 1949 28th Annual Meeting	Hotel Hollenden, Cleveland, Ohio
Harold Simmerman Wenonah, N.J. 14th President	Dec. 16–19, 1950 29th Annual Meeting	Drake Hotel, Chicago, Ill.
Harold Simmerman	Dec. 8–11, 1951 30th Annual Meeting	Hotel New Yorker, New York, N.Y.
Meredith W. Morgan Richmond, Calif. 15th President	Dec. 7–10, 1952 31st Annual Meeting	Seneca Hotel, Rochester, N.Y.
Meredith W. Morgan	Dec. 5–8, 1953 32d Annual Meeting	Drake Hotel, Chicago, Ill.
John D. Perry Winston-Salem, N.C. 16th President	Dec. 11–14, 1954 33d Annual Meeting	Royal York Hotel, Toronto, Ont., Canada
John D. Perry	Dec. 7–13, 1955 34th Annual Meeting	Drake Hotel, Chicago, Ill.
Robert W Tubesing Richmond, Ind. 17th President	Dec. 5–11, 1956 35th Annual Meeting	Shamrock-Hilton Hotel, Houston, Tex.
Robert W. Tubesing	Dec. 4–10, 1957 36th Annual Meeting	Drake Hotel, Chicago, Ill.
Lawrence Fitch Philadelphia, Pa. 18th President	Dec. 10–16, 1958 37th Annual Meeting	Statler Hotel, Boston, Mass.
Lawrence Fitch	Dec. 9–15, 1959 38th Annual Meeting	Drake Hotel, Chicago, Ill.
Ralph C. Wick Rapid City, S.Dak. 19th President	Dec. 7–13, 1960 39th Annual Meeting	Sheraton-Palace Hotel, San Francisco, Calif.
Ralph C. Wick	Dec. 6–12, 1961 40th Annual Meeting	Drake Hotel, Chicago, Ill.
Donald Springer Anniston, Ala. 20th President	Dec. 5–11, 1962 41st Annual Meeting	Deauville Hotel, Miami, Fla.
Donald Springer	Dec. 4–10, 1963 42d Annual Meeting	Drake Hotel, Chicago, Ill.
J. Donald Kratz Souderton, Pa. 21st President	Dec. 9–15, 1964 43d Annual Meeting	Columbus Plaza Hotel, Columbus, Ohio
J. Donald Kratz	Dec. 8–14, 1965 44th Annual Meeting	Drake Hotel, Chicago, Ill.
Monroe J. Hirsch Ojai, Calif. 22d President	Dec. 7–13, 1966 45th Annual Meeting	Denver Hilton Hotel, Denver, Colo.

Monroe J. Hirsch	Dec. 7–12, 1967 46th Meeting	Drake Hotel, Chicago, Ill.
Edward J. Fisher Waterloo, Ont., Canada 23d President	Dec. 5–10, 1968 47th Annual Meeting	Beverly Hilton Hotel, Beverly Hills, Calif.
Edward J. Fisher	Dec. 11–16, 1969 48th Annual Meeting	Bellevue Stratford Hotel, Philadelphia, Pa.
John Zettel Cincinnati, Ohio 24th President	Dec. 10–15, 1970 49th Annual Meeting	Deauville Hotel, Miami, Fla.
John Zettel	Dec. 9–14, 1971 50th Annual Meeting	Royal York Hotel, Toronto, Ont., Canada
Henry B. Peters Birmingham, Ala. 25th President	Dec. 14–19, 1972 51st Annual Meeting	Waldorf-Astoria Hotel, New York, N.Y.
Henry B. Peters	Dec. 6–11, 1973 52d Annual Meeting	Fairmont Hotel, San Francisco, Calif.
Garland W. Clay Ardmore, Okla. 26th President	Dec. 14–17, 1974 53d Annual Meeting	Deauville Hotel, Miami, Fla.
Garland W. Clay	Dec. 11–16. 1975 54th Annual Meeting	Sheraton Hotel, Columbus, Ohio
Frederick W. Baublitz Martinsville, Va. 27th President	Dec. 9–14, 1976 55th Annual Meeting	Portland-Hilton Hotel, Portland, Oreg.
Frederick W. Baublitz	Dec. 8–13, 1977 56th Annual Meeting	Birmingham Hyatt Hotel, Birmingham, Ala.
Bradford W. Wild Birmingham, Ala. 28th President	Dec. 7–12, 1978 57th Annual Meeting	Sheraton Hotel, Boston, Mass.
Bradford W. Wild	Dec. 6–11, 1979 58th Annual Meeting	Disneyland Hotel, Anaheim, Calif.
Merton C. Flom Houston, Tex. 29th President	Dec. 11–16, 1980 59th Annual Meeting	Drake Hotel, Chicago, Ill.
Merton C. Flom	Dec. 10–15, 1981 60th Annual Meeting	Sheraton Twin Towers Hotel, Orlando, Fla.
Gordon G. Heath Bloomington, Ind. 30th President	Dec. 9–14, 1982 61st Annual Meeting	Franklin Plaza Hotel, Philadelphia, Pa.
Gordon G. Heath	Dec. 8–13, 1983 62d Annual Meeting	Hyatt Regency Hotel, Houston, Tex.
Melvin D. Wolfberg Philadelphia, Pa. 31st President	Dec. 6–11, 1984 63d Annual Meeting	Clarion Hotel, St. Louis, Mo.
Melvin D. Wolfberg	Dec. 7–10, 1985 64th Annual Meeting	Peach Tree Plaza Hotel, Atlanta, Ga.

Frank A. Brazelton	Dec. 11–16, 1986	Harbour Castle Hotel,
Fullerton, Calif.	65th Annual Meeting	Toronto, Ont., Canada
32d President		

SECRETARIES*

AMERICAN ACADEMY OF OPTOMETRY

Carel C. Koch, June 1922–December 1925 and December 1944–December 1973
Charles E. Cox, December 1925–December 1927
J. Fred Andreae, December 1927–December 1944
John N. Schoen, December 1973–December 1982
Frank A. Brazelton, December 1982–December 1984
Bert C. Corwin, December 1984–December 1986
N. Rex Ghormley, December 1986–

*The office was designated as *secretary* from 1928 until 1956 when it was changed to *secretary-treasurer*, although the secretary also functioned as the treasurer. From December 1922 to December 1925 there was a separate office of *treasurer*, held by E.E. Fielding. From December 1925 to December 1928 the combined term *secretary-treasurer* was used for the secretary.

OFFICERS AND EXECUTIVE COUNCIL MEMBERS

AMERICAN ACADEMY OF OPTOMETRY

June 2–December 19, 1922

CHAIRMAN
M. Steinfeld, Paducah, Ky.

VICE-CHAIRMAN
C.S. Brown, Richmond, Mo.

SECRETARY-TREASURER
Carel C. Koch, Minneapolis, Minn.

December 19, 1922–December 11, 1923 *

CHAIRMAN
M. Steinfeld, Paducah, Ky.

VICE-CHAIRMAN
C.S. Brown, Richmond, Mo.

SECRETARY
Carel C. Koch, Minneapolis, Minn.

TREASURER
E.E. Fielding, Omaha, Nebr.

COUNCIL MEMBERS
Ernest Petry, Rochester, N.Y.
Charles Sheard, Rochester, Minn.
E. LeRoy Ryer, New York, N.Y.

December 11, 1923–June 11, 1924

CHAIRMAN
E.G. Wiseman, Buffalo, N.Y.

VICE-CHAIRMAN
H. Bestor, Rochester, N.Y.

SECRETARY
Carel C. Koch, Minneapolis, Minn.

TREASURER
E.E. Fielding, Omaha, Nebr.

COUNCIL MEMBERS
Ernest Petry, Rochester, N.Y.
E. LeRoy Ryer, New York, N.Y.
Charles Sheard, Rochester, Minn.

June 11, 1924–December 14, 1925

CHAIRMAN
Eugene G. Wiseman, Buffalo, N.Y.

VICE-CHAIRMAN
E. LeRoy Ryer, New York, N.Y.

SECRETARY
Carel C. Koch, Minneapolis, Minn.

TREASURER
E.E. Fielding, Omaha, Nebr.

COUNCIL MEMBERS
Charles Sheard, Rochester, Minn.
Harry Bestor, Rochester, N.Y.

December 14, 1925–December 7, 1926

CHAIRMAN
Eugene G. Wiseman, Buffalo, N.Y.

VICE-CHAIRMAN
B.W. Hazell, Baltimore, Md.

SECRETARY-TREASURER
Charles E. Cox, Rochester, N.Y.

COUNCIL MEMBERS
Ernest Petry, Rochester, N.Y.
M. Steinfeld, Paducah, Ky.

December 7, 1926–December 6, 1927

CHAIRMAN
E.G. Wiseman, Buffalo, N.Y.

VICE-CHAIRMAN
B.W. Hazell, Baltimore, Md.

SECRETARY-TREASURER
Charles E. Cox, Rochester, N.Y.

COUNCIL MEMBERS
M. Steinfeld, Paducah, Ky.
E. Petry, Rochester, N.Y.
C.C. Koch, Minneapolis, Minn.
W.H. Hammond, Lockport, N.Y.

* The officers are also members of the Executive Council, but their names are not repeated.

December 6, 1927–December 4, 1928

CHAIRMAN
Eugene G. Wiseman, Buffalo, N.Y.

VICE-CHAIRMAN
B.W. Hazell, Baltimore, Md.

SECRETARY-TREASURER
J. Fred Andreae, Baltimore, Md.

COUNCIL MEMBERS
Frank I. Tibbitts, Little Rock, Ark.
J.H. Drakeford, New York, N.Y.
Carel C. Koch, Minneapolis, Minn.
C.E. Cox, Rochester, N.Y.

December 4, 1928–December 18, 1929

CHAIRMAN
Carel C. Koch, Minneapolis, Minn.

VICE-CHAIRMAN
Elmer E. Hotaling, New York, N.Y.

SECRETARY
J. Fred Andreae, Baltimore, Md.

COUNCIL MEMBERS
W.I. Brown, New Bedford, Mass.
F.I. Tibbits, Little Rock, Ark.
E.G. Silver, Washington, D.C.
A.M. Skeffington, Chicago, Ill.

December 18, 1929–December 16, 1930

CHAIRMAN
Briggs S. Palmer, Boston, Mass.

VICE-CHAIRMAN
O.J. Melvin, Omaha, Nebr.

SECRETARY
Fred Andreae, Baltimore, Md.

COUNCIL MEMBERS
A.M. Skeffington, Chicago, Ill.
R.N. Walker, Winston-Salem, N.C.
C.R. Padelford, Fall River, Mass.
D.H. Pratt, New York, N.Y.

December 16, 1930–December 8, 1931

CHAIRMAN
Walter I. Brown, New Bedford, Mass.

VICE-CHAIRMAN
O.J. Melvin, Omaha, Nebr.

SECRETARY
J. Fred Andreae, Baltimore, Md.

COUNCIL MEMBERS
R.M. Walker, Winston-Salem, N.C.
W.J. Jarvis, Buffalo, N.Y.
S.S. Titus, Kansas City, Mo.
E.B. Alexander, Ducan, Okla.

December 8, 1931–December 20, 1932

CHAIRMAN
Walter I. Brown, New Bedford, Mass.

VICE-CHAIRMAN
O.J. Melvin, Omaha, Nebr.

SECRETARY
J. Fred Andreae, Baltimore, Md.

COUNCIL MEMBERS
D.R. Paine, Topeka, Kans.
J.H. Drakeford, New York, N.Y.
W.S. Farmer, Oklahoma City, Okla.
A.R. Reinke, San Francisco, Calif.

December 20, 1932–December 19, 1933

CHAIRMAN
O.J. Melvin, Omaha, Nebr.

VICE-CHAIRMAN
Robert N. Walker,
Winston-Salem, N.C.

SECRETARY
J. Fred Andreae, Baltimore, Md.

COUNCIL MEMBERS
Walter I. Brown, New Bedford, Mass.
Harry E. Pine, Chicago, Ill.
George W. Keevil,
Toronto, Ont., Canada
William M. Kinney,
Los Angeles, Calif.

December 19, 1933–December 18, 1934

CHAIRMAN
O.J. Melvin, Omaha, Nebr.

VICE-CHAIRMAN
Robert N. Walker,
Winston-Salem, N.C.

SECRETARY
J. Fred Andreae, Baltimore, Md.

COUNCIL MEMBERS
Edwin F. Tait, Philadelphia, Pa.
Richard Hall, Cleveland, Ohio
Jesse Wheeler, Hartford, Conn.
A.R. Reinke, Oakland, Calif.
R.F. Pray, Beaumont, Tex.

December 18, 1934–August 27, 1935

CHAIRMAN
Robert N. Walker,
Winston-Salem, N.C.

VICE-CHAIRMAN
R.M. Hall, Cleveland, Ohio

SECRETARY
J. Fred Andreae, Baltimore, Md.

COUNCIL MEMBERS
O.J. Melvin, Omaha, Nebr.
A.R. Reinke, Oakland, Calif.
Franklin A. Seward, New York, N.Y.
Clarence R. Carlson, Lincoln, Nebr.

August 27, 1935–August 25, 1936

CHAIRMAN
Robert N. Walker,
Winston-Salem, N.C.

VICE-CHAIRMAN
R.M. Hall, Cleveland, Ohio

SECRETARY
J. Fred Andreae, Baltimore, Md.

COUNCIL MEMBERS
D.R. Paine, Topeka, Kans.
William M. Kinney,
Los Angeles, Calif.
Franklin A. Seward, New York, N.Y.
Clarence R. Carlson, Lincoln, Nebr.

August 25, 1936–June 26, 1937

CHAIRMAN
Robert M. Hall, Cleveland, Ohio

VICE-CHAIRMAN
C.R. Carlson, Lincoln, Nebr.

SECRETARY
J. Fred Andreae, Baltimore, Md.

COUNCIL MEMBERS
William M. Kinney,
Los Angeles, Calif.
L.H. Kraskin, Washington, D.C.
D.R. Paine, Topeka, Kans.
Robert N. Walker,
Winston-Salem, N.C.

June 26, 1937–June 24, 1938

CHAIRMAN
Robert M. Hall, Cleveland, Ohio

VICE-CHAIRMAN
Arthur P. Wheelock,
Des Moines, Iowa

SECRETARY
J. Fred Andreae, Baltimore, Md.

COUNCIL MEMBERS
Glenn Winslow, Los Angeles, Calif.
L.H. Kraskin, Washington, D.C.
Don R. Paine, Topeka, Kans.
Benjamin H. Bohall, Oswego, N.Y.

June 24, 1938–June 24, 1939

CHAIRMAN
Don R. Paine, Topeka, Kans.

VICE-CHAIRMAN
Arthur P. Wheelock,
Des Moines, Iowa

SECRETARY
J. Fred Andreae, Baltimore, Md.

COUNCIL MEMBERS
Richard M. Hall, Cleveland, Ohio
Glenn Winslow, Los Angeles, Calif.
B.H. Bohall, Oswego, N.Y.
Elmer E. Hotaling, New York, N.Y.

June 24, 1939–December 10, 1940

CHAIRMAN
Don R. Paine, Topeka, Kans.

VICE-CHAIRMAN
Arthur P. Wheelock,
Des Moines, Iowa

SECRETARY
J. Fred Andreae, Baltimore, Md.

COUNCIL MEMBERS
Richard M. Hall, Cleveland, Ohio
Glenn Winslow, Los Angeles, Calif.
Frances P. Marshall,
Washington, D.C.
Elmer E. Hotaling, New York, N.Y.

December 10, 1940–December 9, 1941

PRESIDENT *
Arthur P. Wheelock,
Des Moines, Iowa

VICE-PRESIDENT
Elmer E. Hotaling, New York, N.Y.

* The title was changed from *chairman* to
president in 1940.

SECRETARY
J. Fred Andreae, Baltimore, Md.

COUNCIL MEMBERS
W. Edward Dewey,
Battle Creek, Mich.
C.R. Wells, Boston, Mass.
Wm. Greenspoon, Bluefield, W.Va.
Glenn Winslow, Los Angeles, Calif.

December 9, 1941–December 12, 1944

PRESIDENT
Arthur P. Wheelock,
Des Moines, Iowa

VICE-PRESIDENT
Curtis R. Wells, Boston, Mass.

SECRETARY
J. Fred Andreae, Baltimore, Md.

COUNCIL MEMBERS
W. Edward Dewey,
Battle Creek, Mich.
Harold Fisher, New York, N.Y.
Wm. Greenspoon, Bluefield, W.Va.
Glenn Winslow, Los Angeles, Calif.

December 12, 1944–May 21, 1947

PRESIDENT
J. Fred Andreae, Baltimore, Md.

VICE-PRESIDENT
Harold M. Fisher, Mt. Kisco, N.Y.

SECRETARY
Carel C. Koch, Minneapolis, Minn.

PAST PRESIDENT
Arthur P. Wheelock,
Des Moines, Iowa

COUNCIL MEMBERS
Robert E. Bannon, Hanover, N.H.
W. Edward Dewey,
Battle Creek, Mich.
D.G. Hummel, Cleveland, Ohio
E.A. Hutchinson, Los Angeles, Calif.

May 21, 1947–December 7, 1948

PRESIDENT
Harold M. Fisher, Mt. Kisco, N.Y.

VICE-PRESIDENT
D.G. Hummel, Cleveland, Ohio

SECRETARY
Carel C. Koch, Minneapolis, Minn.

PAST PRESIDENT
J. Fred Andreae, Baltimore, Md.

COUNCIL MEMBERS
Robert E. Bannon, Hanover, N.H.
John R. Dean, Los Angeles, Calif.
W. Edward Dewey,
Battle Creek, Mich.
Laurence P. Folsom,
South Royalton, Vt.

December 7, 1948–December 19, 1950

PRESIDENT
D.G. Hummel, Cleveland, Ohio

VICE-PRESIDENT
Harold Simmerman, Woodbury, N.J.

SECRETARY
Carel C. Koch, Minneapolis, Minn.

PAST PRESIDENT
Harold Fisher, Mt. Kisco, N.Y.

COUNCIL MEMBERS
Lawrence Fitch, Philadelphia, Pa.
Meredith W. Morgan, Berkeley, Calif.
J.D. Perry, Winston-Salem, N.C.
R.W. Tubesing, Richmond, Ind.

EX OFFICIO MEMBERS
J. Fred Andreae, Baltimore, Md.
Robert E. Bannon, Hanover, N.H.
Arthur P. Wheelock,
Des Moines, Iowa

December 19, 1950–December 10, 1952

PRESIDENT
Harold Simmerman, Woodbury, N.J.

VICE-PRESIDENT
Robert E. Bannon, Hanover, N.H.

SECRETARY
Carel C. Koch, Minneapolis, Minn.

PAST PRESIDENT
D.G. Hummel, Cleveland, Ohio

COUNCIL MEMBERS
Lawrence Fitch, Philadelphia, Pa.
John D. Perry, Jr.,
Winston-Salem, N.C.
R.W. Tubesing, Richmond, Ind.
Ralph E. Wick, Rapid City, S.Dak.

EX OFFICIO MEMBERS
  Harold Fisher, New York, N.Y.
  Meredith W. Morgan, Berkeley, Calif.
  Arthur P. Wheelock,
    Des Moines, Iowa

December 10, 1952–December 14, 1954

PRESIDENT
  Meredith W. Morgan, Berkeley, Calif.

VICE-PRESIDENT
  John D. Perry, Winston-Salem, N.C.

SECRETARY
  Carel C. Koch, Minneapolis, Minn.

PAST PRESIDENT
  Harold Simmerman, Wenonah, N.J.

COUNCIL MEMBERS
  Lawrence Fitch, Philadelphia, Pa.
  Donald A. Springer, Anniston, Ala.
  R.W. Tubesing, Richmond, Ind.
  Ralph E. Wick, Rapid City, S.Dak.

EX OFFICIO MEMBER
  D.G. Hummel, Cleveland, Ohio

December 14, 1954–December 11, 1956

PRESIDENT
  John D. Perry, Jr.,
    Winston-Salem, N.C.

VICE-PRESIDENT
  R.W. Tubesing, Richmond, Ind.

SECRETARY
  Carel C. Koch, Minneapolis, Minn.

PAST PRESIDENT
  Meredith W. Morgan, Berkeley, Calif.

COUNCIL MEMBERS
  Lawrence Fitch, Philadelphia, Pa.
  J. Donald Kratz, Souderton, Pa.
  Donald A. Springer, Anniston, Ala.
  Ralph E. Wick, Rapid City, S.Dak.

EX OFFICIO MEMBER
  Harold Simmerman, Wenonah, N.J.

December 11, 1956–December 16, 1958

PRESIDENT
  Robert W. Tubesing, Richmond, Ind.

VICE-PRESIDENT
  Lawrence Fitch, Philadelphia, Pa.

SECRETARY-TREASURER
  Carel C. Koch, Minneapolis, Minn.

PAST PRESIDENT
  John D. Perry, Winston-Salem, N.C.

COUNCIL MEMBERS
  Ralph E. Wick, Rapid City, S.Dak.
  Donald A. Springer, Anniston, Ala.
  J. Donald Kratz, Souderton, Pa.
  Monroe Hirsch, Ojai, Calif.

EX OFFICIO MEMBERS
  Meredith W. Morgan, Berkeley, Calif.
  Harold Simmerman, Wenonah, N.J.

December 16, 1958–December 13, 1960

PRESIDENT
  Lawrence Fitch, Philadelphia, Pa.

VICE-PRESIDENT
  Ralph E. Wick, Rapid City, S.Dak.

SECRETARY-TREASURER
  Carel C. Koch, Minneapolis, Minn.

PAST PRESIDENT
  Robert W. Tubesing, Richmond, Ind.

COUNCIL MEMBERS
  Donald A. Springer, Anniston, Ala.
  J. Donald Kratz, Souderton, Pa.
  Monroe J. Hirsch, Ojai, Calif.
  Edward J. Fisher,
    Toronto, Ont., Canada

EX OFFICIO MEMBERS
  V.J. Ellerbrock, Columbus, Ohio
  Henry W. Hofstetter,
    Bloomington, Ind.
  Meredith W. Morgan, Berkeley, Calif.
  John D. Perry, Winston-Salem, N.C.
  Harold Simmerman, Wenonah, N.J.

December 13, 1960–December 11, 1961

PRESIDENT
  Ralph E. Wick, Rapid City, S.Dak.

VICE-PRESIDENT
  Donald A. Springer, Anniston, Ala.

SECRETARY
  Carel C. Koch, Minneapolis, Minn.

PAST PRESIDENT
  Lawrence Fitch, Philadelphia, Pa.

Council Members
  J. Donald Kratz, Souderton, Pa.
  Monroe J. Hirsch, Ojai, Calif.
  E.J. Fisher, Toronto, Ont., Canada
  John Zettel, Cincinnati, Ohio

Ex Officio Members
  V.J. Ellerbrock, Columbus, Ohio
  Henry W. Hofstetter,
    Bloomington, Ind.
  Meredith W. Morgan, Berkeley, Calif.
  Robert W. Tubesing, Richmond, Ind.
  Harold Simmerman, Wenonah, N.J.

December 11, 1962–December 15, 1964

President
  Donald Springer, Anniston, Ala.

Vice-President
  J. Donald Kratz, Souderton, Pa.

Secretary-Treasurer
  Carel C. Koch, Minneapolis, Minn.

Council Members
  Monroe J. Hirsch, Ojai, Calif.
  E.J. Fisher, Toronto, Ont., Canada
  John Zettel, Cincinnati, Ohio
  Henry B. Peters, Berkeley, Calif.

Ex Officio Members
  V.J. Ellerbrock, Columbus, Ohio
  Henry W. Hofstetter,
    Bloomington, Ind.
  Meredith W. Morgan, Berkeley, Calif.
  Lawrence Fitch, Philadelphia, Pa.
  Harold Simmerman, Wenonah, N.J.

December 15, 1964–December 13, 1966

President
  J. Donald Kratz, Souderton, Pa.

Vice-President
  Monroe J. Hirsch, Ojai, Calif.

Secretary-Treasurer
  Carel C. Koch, Minneapolis, Minn.

Past President
  Donald A. Springer, Anniston, Ala.

Council Members
  E.J. Fisher, Toronto, Ont., Canada
  John Zettel, Cincinnati, Ohio
  Henry B. Peters, Berkeley, Calif.
  Garland Clay, Ardmore, Okla.

Ex Officio Members
  Ralph E. Wick, Rapid City, S.Dak.
  Bradford Wild, Columbus, Ohio
  Henry W. Hofstetter,
    Bloomington, Ind.
  Meredith W. Morgan, Berkeley, Calif.
  Harold Simmerman, Wenonah, N.J.

December 13, 1966–December 10, 1968

President
  Monroe J. Hirsch, Ojai, Calif.

Vice-President
  E.J. Fisher, Waterloo, Ont., Canada

Secretary
  Carel C. Koch, Minneapolis, Minn.

Past President
  J. Donald Kratz, Souderton, Pa.

Council Members
  John Zettel, Cincinnati, Ohio
  Henry B. Peters, Berkeley, Calif.
  Garland W. Clay, Ardmore, Okla.
  Arthur Shlaifer, Philadelphia, Pa.

Ex Officio Members
  Merton C. Flom, Berkeley, Calif.
  Henry W. Hofstetter,
    Bloomington, Ind.
  Meredith W. Morgan, Berkeley, Calif.
  Harold Simmerman, Wenonah, N.J.
  Donald A. Springer, Anniston, Ala.
  Bradford W. Wild, Columbus, Ohio

First Deputy Secretary
  John N. Schoen, Owatonna, Minn.

Second Deputy Secretary
  Leo Meyer, St. Paul, Minn.

December 10, 1968–December 15, 1970

President
  Edward J. Fisher,
    Waterloo, Ont., Canada

Vice-President
  John Zettel, Cincinnati, Ohio

Secretary
  Carel C. Koch, Minneapolis, Minn.

Past President
  Monroe J. Hirsch, Ojai, Calif.

COUNCIL MEMBERS
Henry B. Peters, Birmingham, Ala.
Garland W. Clay, Ardmore, Okla.
Arthur Shlaifer, Philadelphia, Pa.
Bradford W. Wild,
Forest Grove, Oreg.

EX OFFICIO MEMBERS
Donald Korb (1969), Boston, Mass.
Frederick U. Baublitz (1970),
Martinsville, Va.
Merton C. Flom, Berkeley, Calif.
Henry W. Hofstetter,
Bloomington, Ind.
J. Donald Kratz, Souderton, Pa.
Meredith W. Morgan, Berkeley, Calif.
Harold Simmerman, Sewell, N.J.

FIRST DEPUTY SECRETARY
John N. Schoen, Owatonna, Minn.

SECOND DEPUTY SECRETARY
Leo Meyer, St. Paul, Minn.

December 15, 1970–December 19, 1972

PRESIDENT
John Zettel, Cincinnati, Ohio

VICE-PRESIDENT
Henry B. Peters, Birmingham, Ala.

SECRETARY-TREASURER
Carel C. Koch, Minneapolis, Minn.

PAST PRESIDENT
Edward J. Fisher,
Waterloo, Ont., Canada

COUNCIL MEMBERS
Garland W. Clay, Ardmore, Okla.
Bradford W. Wild,
Forest Grove, Oreg.
Frederick U. Baublitz,
Martinsville, Va.
Merton C. Flom, Berkeley, Calif.

EX OFFICIO MEMBERS
Monroe J. Hirsch, Ojai, Calif.
Henry W. Hofstetter,
Bloomington, Ind.
Meredith W. Morgan, Berkeley, Calif.
John C. Neill, Philadelphia, Pa.
John D. Perry, Winston-Salem, N.C.
Harold Simmerman, Pitman, N.J.

FIRST DEPUTY SECRETARY
John N. Schoen, Owatonna, Minn.

SECOND DEPUTY SECRETARY
Leo Meyer, St. Paul, Minn.

December 19, 1972–December 17, 1974

PRESIDENT
Henry Peters, Birmingham, Ala.

VICE-PRESIDENT
Garland Clay, Ardmore, Okla.

SECRETARY-TREASURER
Carel C. Koch (1973),
Minneapolis, Minn.
John N. Schoen (1974),
Owatonna, Minn.

PAST PRESIDENT
John Zettel, Cincinnati, Ohio

COUNCIL MEMBERS
Bradford Wild,
Forest Grove, Oreg.
Frederick Baublitz, Martinsville, Va.
Merton Flom, Berkeley, Calif.
Gordon Heath, Bloomington, Ind.

EX OFFICIO MEMBERS
Monroe J. Hirsch, Ojai, Calif.
Henry Hofstetter,
Bloomington, Ind.
E.J. Fisher, Waterloo, Ont., Canada
Harold Simmerman, Sewell, N.J.
John D. Perry, Winston-Salem, N.C.
Frederick Hebbard, Columbus, Ohio
Frank A. Brazelton,
Los Angeles, Calif.

December 17, 1974–December 14, 1976

PRESIDENT
Garland W. Clay, Ardmore, Okla.

VICE-PRESIDENT
Frederick U. Baublitz,
Martinsville, Va.

SECRETARY-TREASURER
John N. Schoen, Owatonna, Minn.

PAST PRESIDENT
Henry B. Peters, Birmingham, Ala.

COUNCIL MEMBERS
Merton C. Flom, Berkeley, Calif.
Gordon G. Heath, Bloomington, Ind.
Bradford W. Wild, Birmingham, Ala.
Melvin Wolfberg, Selinsgrove, Pa.

EX OFFICIO MEMBERS
Frank A. Brazelton, Fullerton, Calif.
Monroe J. Hirsch, Ojai, Calif.
Donald G. Pitts, Houston, Tex.
Harold Simmerman, Sewell, N.J.

DEPUTY SECRETARIES
Leo A. Meyer, St. Paul, Minn.
Albert E. Mibeck, Fullerton, Calif.

December 14, 1976–December 12, 1978

PRESIDENT
Frederick Baublitz, Martinsville, Va.

VICE-PRESIDENT
Bradford W. Wild, Birmingham, Ala.

SECRETARY-TREASURER
John N. Schoen, Owatonna, Minn.

PAST PRESIDENT
Garland W. Clay (1977),
Ardmore, Okla.

COUNCIL MEMBERS
Merton C. Flom, Berkeley, Calif.
Gordon G. Heath, Bloomington, Ind.
Melvin Wolfberg, Selinsgrove, Pa.
Frank Brazelton, Fullerton, Calif.
Henry B. Peters (1978),
Birmingham, Ala.

EX OFFICIO MEMBERS
Jess B. Eskridge, Birmingham, Ala.
Frederick W. Hebbard,
Columbus, Ohio
Monroe J. Hirsch, Ojai, Calif.
Donald G. Pitts, Houston, Tex.
Harold Simmerman, Sewell, N.J.

December 12, 1978–December 16, 1980

PRESIDENT
Bradford W. Wild, Birmingham, Ala.

PRESIDENT-ELECT
Merton C. Flom, Berkeley, Calif.

SECRETARY-TREASURER
John M. Schoen, Owatonna, Minn.

PAST PRESIDENT
Frederick U. Baublitz,
Martinsville, Va.

COUNCIL MEMBERS
Gordon G. Heath, Bloomington, Ind.
Melvin D. Wolfberg, Selinsgrove, Pa.
Frank A. Brazelton, Fullerton, Calif.
Bert C. Corwin, Rapid City, S.Dak.

EX OFFICIO MEMBERS
Jess B. Eskridge, Birmingham, Ala.
Theodore P. Grosvenor, Chicago, Ill.
Morris Kirschen, Modesto, Calif.
James W. Walters, Houston, Tex.

December 16, 1980–December 14, 1982

PRESIDENT
Merton C. Flom, Houston, Tex.

PRESIDENT-ELECT
Gordon G. Heath, Bloomington, Ind.

SECRETARY-TREASURER
John N. Schoen, Owatonna, Minn.

IMMEDIATE PAST PRESIDENT
Bradford W. Wild, Birmingham, Ala.

COUNCIL MEMBERS
Melvin D. Wolfberg,
Philadelphia, Pa.
Frank A. Brazelton, Fullerton, Calif.
Bert C. Corwin, Rapid City, S.Dak.
N. Rex Ghormley, St. Louis, Mo.

EX OFFICIO MEMBERS
Irvin M. Borish (1982),
Bloomington, Ind.
Jess B. Eskridge, Birmingham, Ala.
Theodore P. Grosvenor,
Houston, Tex.
Morris Kirschen, Modesto, Calif.
Meredith W. Morgan (1982),
Berkeley, Calif.
James W. Walters (1981),
Houston, Tex.

December 14, 1982–December 11, 1984

PRESIDENT
Gordon G. Heath, Bloomington, Ind.

PRESIDENT-ELECT
Melvin D. Wolfberg,
Philadelphia, Pa.

SECRETARY-TREASURER
Frank A. Brazelton, Fullerton, Calif.

IMMEDIATE PAST PRESIDENT
Merton C. Flom, Houston, Tex.

COUNCIL MEMBERS
Bert C. Corwin, Rapid City, S.Dak.
N. Rex Ghormley, St. Louis, Mo.
Joan E. Exford, Boston, Mass.
Charles J. Krall, Mitchell, S.Dak.

EX OFFICIO MEMBERS
Irvin M. Borish, Houston, Tex.
Jess B. Eskridge, Birmingham, Ala.
Roland E. Gaudette, Spencer, Mass.
Theodore P. Grosvenor,
Houston, Tex.
Morris Kirschen, Modesto, Calif.
Meredith W. Morgan, Berkeley, Calif.

December 11, 1984–December 16, 1986

PRESIDENT
Melvin D. Wolfberg,
Philadelphia, Pa.

PRESIDENT-ELECT
Frank A. Brazelton, Fullerton, Calif.

SECRETARY-TREASURER
Bert C. Corwin, Rapid City, S.Dak.

IMMEDIATE PAST PRESIDENT
Gordon G. Heath, Bloomington, Ind.

COUNCIL MEMBERS
N. Rex Ghormley, St. Louis, Mo.
Joan E. Exford, Boston, Mass.
Charles J. Krall, Mitchell, S.Dak.
Anthony P. Cullen,
Waterloo, Ont., Canada

December 16, 1986–

PRESIDENT
Frank Brazelton, Fullerton, Calif.

PRESIDENT-ELECT
Bert C. Corwin, Rapid City, S.Dak.

SECRETARY-TREASURER
N. Rex Ghormley, St. Louis, Mo.

IMMEDIATE PAST PRESIDENT
Melvin Wolfberg, Philadelphia, Pa.

COUNCIL MEMBERS
Joan E. Exford, Boston, Mass.
Anthony P. Cullen,
Waterloo, Ont., Canada
Gerald E. Lowther, Big Rapids, Mich.
Robert D. Newcomb, Columbus, Ohio

AWARDS[1]

AMERICAN ACADEMY OF OPTOMETRY

The Academy honors individuals who have distinguished themselves in visual science and/or who have been outstanding in leadership and achievement in the field of vision care. Awards are made at the annual meetings in a variety of categories, listed here alphabetically:

GARLAND W. CLAY AWARD

Established in 1978, this plaque award is presented to the person who, in the previous year, published the most significant paper on clinical optometry in the *American Journal of Optometry and Physiological Optics*. The selection is made by the *Journal's* Editorial Council based on originality, clinical relevance, integrity of the research, and the quality of the presentation.

RECIPIENTS

1978	Gillray L. Kandall	1983	Dennis M. Levi
	Paul E. Grattan		Roland S. Harwerth
	Harold E. Bedell	1984	Kenneth A. Polse
1979	James E. Sheedy		Richard J. Brand
	James Saladin		Roderick J. Keener
1980	George Smith		Joan S. Schwalbe
	David A. Atchinson		David W. Vastine
	Nathan Efron	1985	Anthony J. Adams
1981	Clifton M. Schor		James E. Bailey
1982	Patricia Apkarian		Lorance W. Harwood
	Christopher W. Tyler	1986	Ian F. Gutteridge
	Dennis M. Levi		

EMINENT SERVICE AWARD

First presented in 1960 and again in 1961, then not until 1975, this award is granted to a person who has rendered distinguished, exemplary, or unique service to the Academy. Nominations can be made by any Fellow of the Academy to the Chairman of the Awards Committee. The Awards Committee then makes its recommendation to the Academy's Executive Council.

RECIPIENTS

1960	Paul Yarwood	1978	Robert E. Bannon
1961	Daniel G. Hummel	1979	Harold M. Fisher
1975	Merton C. Flom	1982	John N. Schoen
	Mervyn H. Kauhl		
1977	Grace Weiner		
	Harold Simmerman		

WILLIAM FEINBLOOM AWARD

This annual award is presented to an individual who has made a distinguished and significant contribution to clinical excellence and the direct clinical advancement of visual and optometric service, and thus the visual enhancement of the public. The award is not limited to Academy Fellows or to optometrists. The Awards Committee selects one person and submits a recommendation to the Executive Council for approval.

RECIPIENTS

1983	Edward I. Goodlaw	1985	Irvin M. Borish
1984	Morton D. Sarver	1986	Donald R. Korb

GLENN A. FRY
INVITED LECTURE AWARD

Established in 1970, it was jointly sponsored by the American Academy of Optometry and the American Optometric Foundation. The award recognizes a distinguished scientist or clinician for his or her current research contribution by inviting the individual to present a special paper at the annual meeting of the American Academy of Optometry. The recipient presents a lecture on a current research topic of high relevancy to optometry.

RECIPIENTS

1970 Anthony Adams, University of California, Berkeley
     Arthur Afanador,* University of California, Berkeley
1971 Jay Enoch, Washington University, St. Louis
1972 Elwin Marg, University of California, Berkeley
1973 Penelope K. Flom,* University of California, Berkeley
1975 Geoffey H. Henry, Australian National University
1976 Robert E. Marc, University of California, Los Angeles
1977 Donald G. Pitts, University of Houston
1978 Richard Held, Massachusetts Institute of Technology
1979 Gilbert D. McCann, California Institute of Technology
1980 Ronald Harwerth, University of Houston
1981 Carl Kupfer, National Eye Institute
1982 Davida Y. Teller, University of Washington
1983 Richard M. Hill, The Ohio State University
1984 Jacob G. Sivak, University of Waterloo
1985 Clifton Schor, University of California, Berkeley
1986 Ian Bailey, University of California, Berkeley

* Awards based on selection of the best paper presented at the meeting. All other recipients were lecturers invited by the Papers and Program Committee.

HONORARY LIFE FELLOWSHIPS

The award is usually given to a person who has contributed significantly to the Academy or to the art and science of optometry, with years of service being a factor in the selection. Life Fellowships have been awarded on several occasions to individuals who were not optometrists and were not members of the Academy. The Awards Committee makes the recommendations to the Executive Council, which makes the final choice:

RECIPIENTS

1945	Alpheus Smith	1972	John Perry
1947	James P. Southall		Carel C. Koch
	Frederic A. Woll	1973	Harold Simmerman
1949	Julius Neumueller	1974	Lawrence Fitch
1951	William L. Benedict		J.L. Saks
1953	Charles Sheard	1975	Glenn A. Fry
1955	Albert Fitch		Mervyn H. Kauhl
1957	E. Leroy Ryer		Harold M. Fisher
1959	Ralph Minor	1976	Richard M. Hall
1960	Frank Weymouth	1979	Leo A. Meyer
1961	Morris Steinfeld		Henry W. Hofstetter
	J. Fred Andreae		Meredith W. Morgan
1962	Eugene Wiseman	1980	Robert E. Bannon
	Arthur Hoare		Eric Bateman
1965	Kenneth B. Stoddard		Lois B. Bing
1970	Arthur P. Wheelock		Irvin M. Borish
1971	George T. Brooks		Edward J. Fisher
	Russell Manwiller		Daniel G. Hummel
	William Feinbloom	1981	Monroe J. Hirsch
	John Neill		
	William Policoff		

CAREL C. KOCH MEMORIAL AWARD

Established in 1974, this award is presented to a person who has made outstanding contributions to interprofessional relations. This award is not limited to Academy Fellows nor to optometrists, but may be presented to others who have made outstanding contributions in interprofessional relations worthy of national attention.

RECIPIENTS

1974 Henry B. Peters, University of Alabama, Birmingham
1975 Richard J. Ball, Michigan State University
1976 Thomas W. Mou, Virginia Associate Chancellor of Health Sciences
1977 Albert N. Lemoine, University of Kansas
1981 Martha L. Phillips, U.S. Veterans Administration
1982 J. Harold Bailey, Executive Director Emeritus, American Optometric Association
1983 Natalie C. Barraga, University of Texas, Austin
1986 John Hogness, Association of American Health Centers

NEUMUELLER AWARD IN OPTICS

Established in 1969, this annual award is made to an undergraduate student pursuing an optometry degree, who submits a paper not exceeding 3,000 words on one of the following subjects: geometrical optics, physical optics, ophthalmic optics, or optics of the eye. The cash award varies in amount each year according to the earnings from the trust set up for the Academy by Julius Neumueller.

RECIPIENTS

1971	David Fox	1981	Marcie E. Arnesty
	Peter M. Smith		Patsy L. Harvey
1972	Kerry A. Horner	1982	David C. Moline
1973	Donald Wright	1983	Randall Faunce
1974	Paul Wilson	1985	Donald Ferro
1975	Robert Gilman		Reva C. Strumwasser
1976	David N. Schultz	1986	Susan M. Brunnett
1977	Steven A. Wood		Mitchell Munson
1978	Larry M. DeDonato		
	Thomas C. Sather		

CHARLES F. PRENTICE MEDAL AWARD

Established in 1958, this award is presented to an outstanding scientist who has contributed significantly to the advancement of knowledge in the visual sciences. He need not be a Fellow of the Academy, nor an optometrist, nor be a resident of the United States. The recipient of the Prentice Medal is expected to present a scientific paper to the annual Academy meeting.

RECIPIENTS AND TITLES OF THEIR PAPERS

1963 William A.H. Rushton, Ph.D., Sc.D., University of Cambridge, England. "Colour Blindness and Cone Pigments"[2]

1964 Glenn A. Fry, Optometrist, Ph.D., Director, School of Optometry, Ohio State University. "Mechanisms Subserving Color Vision"[3]

1967 Meredith W. Morgan, Optometrist, Ph.D., Dean, School of Optometry, University of California, Berkeley. "Accommodation and Vergence"[4]

1971 Oscar W. Richards, Ph.D., Pacific University. "Some Seeing Problems: Spectacles, Color, Driving and Decline From Age and Poor Lighting"[5]

1972 S. Howard Bartley, Ph.D., Michigan State University. "Some Relations Between Optometry and Psychology"[6]

1973 Lorrin A. Riggs, Ph.D., Brown University. "Responses of the Visual System to Fluctuating Patterns"[7]

1974 Jay M. Enoch, Optometrist, Ph.D., College of Medicine, University of Florida. "Marked Accommodation, Retinal Stretch, Monocular Space Perception and Retinal Receptor Orientation"[8]

1975 Herbert Schober, Ph.D., Institute of Medical Optics, University of Munich. The award was presented posthumously and no paper was published as a Prentice Memorial Lecture.

1976 Henry W. Hofstetter, Optometrist, Ph.D., School of Optometry, Indiana University. "Optometry Curriculum Patterns In Europe"[9]

1977 William D. Wright, D.Sc., Imperial College, London University, England. "The Fundamentals of Color Perception"[10]

1978 Monroe J. Hirsch, Optometrist, Ph.D., Dean, School of Optometry, University of California, Berkeley. The published papers of Hirsch's lecture carried no title other than "Prentice Memorial Lecture," though it dealt with the etiology of myopia.[11]

1980   Sylvester K. Guth, Engineer, D.O.S., General Electric Company. "The Science of Seeing — A Search for Criteria"[12]

1981   Elwin Marg, Optometrist, Ph.D., School of Optometry, University of California, Berkeley. "Is the Animal Model for Stimulus Deprivation Amblyopia in Children Valid or Useful?"[13]

1983   Irving Fatt, Ph.D., School of Optometry, University of California, Berkeley. "Contact Lens Wettability — Myths, Mysteries, and Reality"[14]

1984   Tom N. Cornsweet, Ph.D., School of Social Sciences, University of California, Irvine. "A Simple Retinal Mechanism That Has Complex and Profound Effects on Perception"[15]

1985   Yves Le Grand, Ph.D., Museum National d'Histoire Naturelle, Paris, France. Dr. Le Grand was too ill to attend and the medal was presented to one of his former graduate students, Sami El Hage, at the Sixth-Fourth Annual Meeting. No paper was published as a Prentice Memorial Lecture.

1986   Gerald Westheimer, Optometrist, Ph.D., School of Optometry, University of California, Berkeley. "Visual Acuity and Hyperacuity: Resolution vs. Localization."[16]

References

1. These lists are based upon —
   Am J Optom Arch Am Acad Optom, Jan 1954;31(1):47
   Am J Optom Physiol Opt, Jan 1984;61(1): 61–62
   Am J Optom Physiol Opt, Sept 1984;61(1)9: 613–616
   Directory of Academy Members, Nov 1985.
2. Am J Optom Arch Am Acad Optom, May 1964;41(5):265–282.
3. Am J Optom Arch Am Acad Optom, May 1965;42(5):271–287.
4. Am J Optom Arch Am Acad Optom, July 1968;45(7):417–454.
5. Am J Optom Arch Am Acad Optom, July 1972;49(7):539–546.
6. Am J Optom Arch Am Acad Optom, July 1973;50(7):521–532.
7. Am J Optom Physiol Opt, Oct 1974;51(10):725–735.
8. Am J Optom Physiol Opt, June 1975;52(6):376–392.
9. Am J Optom Physiol Opt, March 1977;54(3):133–141.
10. Am J Optom Physiol Opt, Dec 1977;54(12):801–808.
11. Am J Optom Physiol Opt, March 1979;56(3):177–183.
12. Am J Optom Physiol Opt, Oct 1981;58(10):870–885.
13. Am J Optom Physiol Opt, June 1982;59(6):451–464.
14. Am J Optom Physiol Opt, July 1984;61(7):419–430.
15. Am J Optom Physiol Opt, July 1985;62(7):427–438.
16. Paper not yet published as of July 1987.

CHARLES F. PRENTICE

HENRY W HOFSTETTER
1976

WILLIAM A.H.
RUSHTON 1963

GLENN A. FRY
1964

JAY M. ENOCH
1974

LORRIN A. RIGGS
1973

S. HOWARD BARTLEY
1972

OSCAR W. RICHARDS
1971

MEREDITH W. MORGA
1967

MEDAL AWARD RECIPIENTS*

GERALD WESTHEIMER
1986

WILLIAM D. WRIGHT
1977

YVES LE GRAND
1985

MONROE J. HIRSCH
1978

TOM N. CORNSWEET
1984

IRVING FATT
1983

ELWIN MARG
1981

SYLVESTER K. GUTH
1980

*Photo of 1975 recipient, Herbert Schober, not available.

CHARTER MEMBERS
American Academy of Optometry (1923)

H.M. Bestor, Rochester, N.Y.
H.R. Barnes, Brooklyn, N.Y.
G.A. Barron, Boston, Mass.
C.S. Brown, Richmond, Mo.
A.J. Cross, New York, N.Y.
M.C. Davies, Columbus, Ohio
P.A. Dillworth, New York, N.Y.
A.P. DeKeyser, Portland, Oreg.
L.L. DeMars, Minneapolis, Minn.
H.C. Doane, Boston, Mass.
E.E. Fielding, Red Oak, Iowa
L.P. Folsom, So. Royalton, Vt.
I. Geiger, Sedalia, Mo.
A.C. Hoffman, Minneapolis, Minn.
E.E. Hotaling, New York, N.Y.
P.H. Howard, St. Louis, Mo.
T.M. Howe, Louisville, Ky.
N.Y. Hull, New York, N.Y.
W.B. Irvine, Springfield, Ill.
C.C. Koch, Minneapolis, Minn.

J.I. Kurtz, Minneapolis, Minn.
F. McFadden, Athol, Mass.
G.W. McFatrich, Chicago, Ill.
W.G. Maybee, Toronto, Ont., Canada
W.B. Needles, Kansas City, Kans.
Max Poser, Rochester, N.Y.
J.I. Pascal, New York, N.Y.
Ernest Petry, Rochester, N.Y.
E. LeRoy Ryer, New York, N.Y.
S.H. Robinson, Prescott, Ariz.
F.D. Seward, New York, N.Y.
Chas. Sheard, Southbridge, Mass.
E. Schmidt, Washington, Mo.
R.I. Searfoss, Odessa, Mo.
M. Steinfeld, Paducah, Ky.
W.S. Todd, Hartford, Conn.
L.H. Tully, Evansville, Ind.
D. Truax, Wichita, Kans.
E.G. Wiseman, Buffalo, N.Y.
W.A. Zeitler, St. Louis, Mo.

FIRST CONSTITUTION AND BYLAWS

AMERICAN ACADEMY OF OPTOMETRY

[Adopted in Kansas City, Missouri, June 1924]

ARTICLE 1. NAME

The name of this organization shall be, "The American Academy of Optometry."

ARTICLE 2. OBJECT

The object of the Academy shall be: To unite optometrists of recognized professional ability and ethical standing for the purpose of affording them opportunities for educational advancement; to establish a standard of optometric practice; to encourage and assist optometric research; and to work along all lines to raise the standard of optometric practice, education and ethics.

ARTICLE 3. OFFICERS

The officers of the Academy shall be: A. Chairman, Vice-Chairman, Secretary-Treasurer, and Executive Council which shall consist of the officers and four other members; all to be elected at the annual meeting of the Academy and to serve until the next annual meeting or until their successors are elected.

ARTICLE 4. FELLOWSHIP

Fellowship in the Academy shall be restricted to optometrists and scientists of recognized professional ability, and ethical standing, who shall be elected to fellowship as provided in the by-laws.

ARTICLE 5. AMENDMENTS

This Constitution may be amended at any annual meeting of the Academy by a vote of two-thirds of the members present entitled to vote.

BY-LAWS

ARTICLE 1. DUTIES OF OFFICERS

Section 1. The Chairman shall preside at all meetings of the Academy and shall be Chairman of the Executive Council. He shall appoint all committees and shall perform the duties usually devolving on the office, and as may be directed by the Academy.

Section 2. The Vice-Chairman shall perform the duties of the Chairman in his absence or inability to serve.

Section 3. The Secretary-Treasurer shall keep a record of all proceedings of the Academy and of the Executive Council, conduct correspondence, collect dues, notify the Fellows of the Academy regarding meetings a reasonable time in advance of same, and perform such other duties as pertain to his office, or as may be prescribed by these laws. He shall keep all money of the Academy and disburse same upon signed order of the Chairman, keeping a correct account of all his transactions and reporting same at each annual meeting, or when required by the Chairman, and make a full detailed report of the financial affairs of the Academy, and shall at the expiration of his term of office deliver to his successor all funds, papers and books relative thereto.

Section 4. The Secretary-Treasurer shall furnish bond in such amount as may be required by the Executive Council, the expense of which shall be paid by the Academy.

Section 5. The Executive Council shall transact all business for the Academy and carry out the actions for the Academy at its annual meetings. It shall issue all invitations to become candidates, and shall pass on all these presented by candidates; it shall audit the books of the Secretary-Treasurer and perform such duties usual to an Executive Council. On all matters a majority vote of the council shall prevail except in inviting candidates to fellowship and passing on these in which case a unanimous vote of the council shall be necessary.

ARTICLE 2. ELECTION TO FELLOWSHIP

Section 1. Names suggested for fellowship must be handed to the Secretary and by him sent to each member of the Executive Council who shall investigate the character, standing and ability of the person suggested. After so doing they shall instruct the Chairman to invite the person, providing accepted, to become a candidate for Fellowship. If the person invited accepts, he becomes a "Fellow of the American Academy of Optometry" (F.A.A.O.). The Executive Council may at its discretion waive the writing and delivering of a thesis in person.

Section 2. Each candidate for fellowship in the Academy before receiving fellowship, shall subscribe to the following pledge:

Realizing that the American Academy of Optometry was founded in order to establish a distinctive nucleus composed of practicing optometrists who are endeavoring to develop and maintain the highest ideals and practices of professional life, to the end that optometric science may be further developed, optometric practice elevated and optometric prestige enhanced, I pledge myself as a condition of fellowship in the Academy earnestly to strive to live and practice in absolute accordance with its principles, declarations and regulations.

With Relation to Consultants. Specifically, I promise to strive for perfect knowledge and skill in all recognized branches of optometric and allied sciences; to maintain an open mind to all new developments in them; assiduously to apply this knowledge in conscientiously striving to aid my consultants.

I promise to avoid, as well as my nature permits, selfishness in my dealings with consultants; never to suggest the purchase of service or material things unless the possible advantage of such acquisition to the consultant is clearly evident, and yet fearlessly to advise the adoption of such scientific arts and appliances within my province as will insure the consultant's comfort, satisfaction and well being.

With Relation to Fellow Members. I promise so to conduct my work as to reflect credit upon my profession and my fellow members in the Academy. Pursuant with this object, I will, in my contact with laymen, lend emphasis to the scientific side of optometric work and subordinate the commercial element. I will conduct my work in an office, not a store; display no merchandise or pictures of merchandise in my reception or examination room until after the examination has been concluded.

I will charge such fees as are consistent with the service rendered and with established custom among scientific refractionists, avoiding both nominal fees and fees so unwarrantedly high as to bring discredit upon my fellow members. On the other hand, I reserve the privilege of obeying charitable impulses in occasional cases.

I will not, in seeking publicity, utilize display advertisements in newspapers, or even less credible forms of advertising, such as bill-boards, blotters, novelties, handbills, etc.

I pledge myself scrupulously to regard the legitimate interests of my fellow practitioners, and to refrain from unwarranted criticism but I hold it my duty to condemn flagrant violations of justice to a consultant, gross dereliction in scientific procedure, and general conduct inconsistent with a reasonably high type of professional practice.

When contemplating an act, the consistency of which with Academy rules and regulations is in doubt, I will submit detailed statements concerning same to three Fellows for approval and will abide by their decision.

I pledge myself at all opportunities to advance the influence of the American Academy of Optometry and its individual members.

ARTICLE 3. DUES AND ASSESSMENTS

Section 1. The annual dues of the Academy shall be fifteen dollars ($15.00), payable in advance, on January 1st of each year. Applicants receiving fellowship at any mid-year meeting shall pay dues for the year during which they were admitted.

Section 2. The fee for the fellowship degree and certificate of the American Academy of Optometry shall be ten dollars ($10.00). This fee, together with at least one-half the yearly dues, should accompany the application.

Section 3. The Academy may, at the annual meetings, by a vote of seventy-five per cent of the fellows present who are entitled to vote, levy an assessment for the work of the following year, which shall be binding on each and every Fellow of the Academy.

Section 4. No Fellow of the Academy who is in arrears shall hold office in this Academy, nor shall any vote of any fellow in arrears be counted.

Section 5. Any Fellow of the Academy whose dues and assessments are not paid on February 1st following that on which they are due shall stand suspended, and he shall not receive any reports of meetings, etc., which may be sent to members. If dues are not paid by May 1st his fellowship in the Academy shall cease, and he shall be notified by the Secretary. However, he may become reinstated by paying all arrearages within ten days.

ARTICLE 4. MISCELLANEOUS

Section 1. Any Fellow of the Academy may, and it shall be the duty of each officer of this Academy to prefer charges against any other Fellow who violates any of these By-Laws or the Constitution of this Academy or is alleged to be guilty of unprofessional, dishonest, disloyal or unethical conduct. Charges must be filed in writing with the Secretary, who shall at once furnish the accused and each member of the Executive Council a copy of the same.

Section 2. The Executive Council shall investigate the charges and if they think the charges sustained then shall instruct the Secretary to notify the accused to appear at the next annual meeting for trial. Such notice must be given at least thirty days before the meeting, but if not present, he may be tried in his absence.

Section 3. It shall require a vote of seventy-five per cent of the Fellows present entitled to vote to convict a Fellow of charges, and such conviction shall deprive him of Fellowship in the Academy.

ARTICLE 5. MEETINGS

Section 1. The annual meeting of the Academy shall be held yearly during November or December, the time and place to be decided at the previous annual meeting. Should the Academy fail to select the time and place, the Executive Council shall do so, but said selection must be made at least sixty days prior to the meeting.

Section 2. Educational meetings may be held during the year so directed by the Academy at the annual meeting. No business may be transacted at these meetings, but fellowships may be conferred.

ARTICLE 6. AMENDMENTS

Section 1. These By-Laws may be amended at an annual meeting of the Academy by a two-thirds vote of the Fellows present entitled to vote.

FELLOWSHIP PLEDGE

AMERICAN ACADEMY OF OPTOMETRY (1945)*

Realizing that the American Academy of Optometry was founded in order to establish a distinctive nucleus composed of practicing optometrists who are endeavoring to develop and maintain the highest ideals and practices of professional life, to the end that optometric science may be further developed, optometric practices elevated, and optometric prestige enhanced, I pledge myself as a condition of Fellowship in the Academy earnestly to strive to live and to practice in absolute accordance with its principles, declarations, and regulations.

WITH RELATION TO PATIENTS:

Specifically, I promise to strive for perfect knowledge and skill in all recognized branches of optometric and allied sciences; to maintain an open mind to all new developments in them; and assiduously to apply this knowledge in conscientiously striving to aid my patients.

I promise to avoid selfishness in my dealings with patients; never to suggest the purchase of service or material things unless the possible advantage to the patient of such acquisition is clearly evident; and yet fearlessly to advise the adoption of such scientific arts and appliances within my province as well as to insure the patient's comfort, satisfaction, and well being.

WITH RELATION TO FELLOW MEMBERS:

I promise so to conduct my work as to reflect credit upon my profession and my fellow members in the Academy. Pursuant with this object, I will, in my contact with laymen, lend emphasis to the scientific side of optometric work and subordinate any commercial element. I will conduct my practice in an office and display no merchandise or pictures of merchandise in my reception or examination room.

I will charge such fees as are consistent with the service rendered and in accordance with established custom among scientific refractionists, avoiding both nominal fees and fees so unwarrantedly high as to bring discredit upon my fellow members. On the other hand, I reserve the privilege of obeying charitable impulses in occasional cases.

I will not, in seeking publicity, utilize display advertisements in newspapers, or even less creditable forms of advertising (such as bill-boards, blotters, novelties, hand-bills, etc.).

I pledge myself scrupulously to regard the legitimate interests of my fellow practitioners, and to refrain from unwarranted criticism, but I hold it my duty to condemn flagrant violations of justice to a patient, gross dereliction in scientific procedure, and general conduct inconsistent with a reasonably high type of professional practice.

When contemplating an act which may be inconsistent with the Academy rules and regulations, I will submit detailed statements concerning same to the Executive Council for approval and will abide by their decision.

MEMBERSHIP AGREEMENT

AMERICAN ACADEMY OF OPTOMETRY

[Agreement To Be Signed By Fellow Prior To Receiving His Certificate]

The fellowship certificate granted, being the property of the American Academy of Optometry, every fellow who obtains one must agree and subscribe to the following conditions:

1. That said fellowship certificate is the sole property of the American Academy of Optometry, and that he will not assign, transfer, or part with same.

2. That the said fellowship certificate is conferred upon him personally and not on any other person associated with him.

3. That the said fellowship certificate shall not be carried about for commercial purposes, but shall remain in his personal possession at his office; it can be framed and hung on wall of refracting room, not elsewhere.

4. That the said fellowship certificate shall not be reproduced, altered, or added to in any way, except with the consent of the Academy.

5. That the said fellowship certificate shall be returned immediately to the American Academy of Optometry in the event of death, bankruptcy, or lunacy of the holder; and the Academy may withdraw the fellowship certificate either temporarily or permanently in the event of the holder's failure to pay his annual dues or in the event of the holder's committing any breach of the Academy's fellowship qualifications or in the event of the holder's violating any of the Academy's code of ethics.

* AM J OPTOM ARCH AMER ACAD OPTOM JUNE 1945; 22(6):288-289

SYNOPSIS OF CONSENT AGREEMENT
BETWEEN AMERICAN ACADEMY OF OPTOMETRY
AND FEDERAL TRADE COMMISSION*

The American Academy of Optometry ("Academy") has agreed to comply with the terms of a Consent Order issued by the Federal Trade Commission. A Complaint, setting forth the Commission's allegations against the Academy, has also been issued by the Commission. The Academy's agreement to the Consent Order is for settlement purposes only, and does not constitute an admission by the Academy of a law violation. In December 1981, the Academy adopted a set of guidelines that allow advertising by its members, but such guidelines require further amendment.

The Complaint alleges that the Academy maintained and enforced ethical standards and guidelines and interpreted and implemented standards and guidelines which restricted truthful advertising and solicitation by members or prospective members, and prevented members or prospective members from practicing in commercial locations.

The Consent Order requires that the Academy not restrain advertising of prices, products and services, and other forms of solicitation by any optometrist, or any optometrist's choice of practice location. However, the Consent Order does not prohibit the Academy from adopting reasonable ethical guidelines to prevent false or deceptive advertising or uninvited, in-person solicitations of patients whose particular circumstances make them vulnerable to undue influence. The Consent Order also does not restrict the Academy from maintaining standards on the competency of its members.

The Consent Order requires that the Academy not revoke, suspend, or refuse to grant Academy membership, or discipline or penalize any optometrist, without first providing him or her with written notice of any allegations, and a reasonable opportunity to respond to them.

The Consent Order also requires the Academy to remove from its constitution, bylaws, policy statements, and guidelines any provision that is inconsistent with the Consent Order.

This synopsis is not intended to constitute an official interpretation of the Consent Order or Complaint, or to modify in any way their terms.

* Am J Optom Physiol Opt, October 1986; 63(6):857

PERSONAL NAME INDEX*

---

* The name index includes those appearing in Chapters 1 through 8 and the sections on chronology, the *Journal*, and Postgraduate Education in the Appendix but not where there are lists of names of the Presidents, Officers, winners of awards, and lecturers at the 1955 postgraduate education program.

SUBJECT
INDEX

ABOUT THE AUTHOR

JAMES R. GREGG is Professor Emeritus at the Southern California College of Optometry where he served as a lecturer and administrator for thirty-seven years, including one year as Interim Dean. He is a graduate of Ohio State College of Optometry and has received two honorary degrees from SCCO.

In private practice for over twenty-five years, Dr. Gregg also was very active in optometric organizational affairs on the local, state and national levels. He has been president of the California Optometric Association and served the COA in many capacities for a number of years. He received the American Optometric Association's Distinguished Journalism Award in 1972 and the AOA's Distinguished Service Award in 1982.

Author of fifteen books and over 600 articles in more than 200 different journals and magazines, he has also written many newspaper columns, pamphlets and news releases. Thus it is probable that more people have read his writings than any optometrist in history. He has authored three other books dealing with optometric history: *The Story of Optometry* (The Ronald Press 1965), *The American Optometric Association, A History* (AOA 1972) and *The Origin and Development of the Southern California College of Optometry* (SCCO 1984).